A

Harnessing Space

Harnessing

ILLUSTRATED WITH PHOTO-

GRAPHS AND DIAGRAMS

Edited — and with an

Space

Introduction and Commentary

by **WILLY LEY**

The Macmillan Company, New York

Collier-Macmillan Limited, London

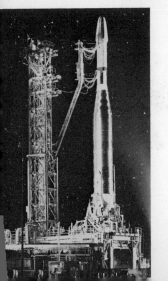

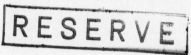

Designed by Jack Meserole

Library of Congress catalog card number: 63–16112

The Macmillan Company, New York
Collier-Macmillan Canada, Ltd., Toronto, Ontario

Printed in the United States of America

Contents

List of Illustrations

List of Tables

Introduction

Introduction

IN THE EVENING HOURS of Wednesday, July 11, 1962, the American public was able to watch, for the first time in history, a live television broadcast from Europe. This broadcast came from England, having been preceded a few hours earlier by a taped television broadcast transmitted directly to the United States from France; both were made possible through the existence of the communication satellite Telstar, which had been launched from Cape Canaveral, Florida, in the morning of the preceding day.

It was not the first broadcast from space. Earlier artificial satellites had broadcast tapes to the ground; these were mainly tapes containing scientific information about nearby space gathered by the instruments in the satellite. Even pictures had been broadcast from space; the Tiros satellites (Tiros I was launched on April 1, 1960) had sent pictures of the earth's cloud cover from space (see pp. 98–100); a Russian rocket that had passed behind the side of the moon always seen from the earth had transmitted a number of photographs of the moon's far side. One satellite had even made broadcasts to the American public—in 1958 an Atlas rocket (Project SCORE) was sent into orbit with a prerecorded Christmas message by President Eisenhower; the rocket also received and rebroadcast other messages (see pp. 42, 130–133).

But while a recorded voice from space was impressive enough, the transmission of a live show from one continent to another via satellite was needed to convince the public that the space sciences and their technology will have a direct influence on daily living.

It is the purpose of this book to point out in what areas of

15

living the influence of the space sciences is likely to be felt first and to show that space scientists have been aware of these potential developments for a number of years.

For mysterious reasons—if there are any reasons at all—a large section of the public has clung stubbornly to the belief that space research is for military purposes only. That there are peaceful applications of space is a statement received by these people with doubt, if not outright disbelief. The simple fact is, of course, that space *also* has military uses, as does the ocean. But the proportion of peaceful activities to the purely military uses of space is about the same as that of the number of warships to commercial vessels on the Atlantic Ocean.

The space sciences, usually referred to as "astronautics," are not quite as young as is believed generally. They have their roots in philosophical speculations, originating in pre-Christian times, about the shape, size, and constitution of the universe. One may say that these conjectures gradually changed into astronomy, and astronomy, in turn, gave birth to astronautics. Four major eras in the development of astronautics can be distinguished: from 1600 to 1900, 1900 to 1925, 1925 to 1945, and the period since then.

During the first of these eras, the astronomical and other scientific foundations were laid. Working from about 1605 to 1608, the German astronomer Johannes Kepler (1571–1630) established the true shape of a planet's orbit, showing that it is an ellipse with the sun as one of its two focal points. (Before this it had been thought by everybody, including the Polish astronomer Nicholas Copernicus (1473–1543) that an orbit was a combination of circular motions.) Kepler also formulated the very important natural law that the line from the center of the sun to the center of the planet, the "radius vector," to use his term, swept over equal areas during equal time intervals. Kepler thus provided the fundamental facts upon which a calculation of an orbit can be based.

Almost precisely eighty years later, in 1687, the English natural philosopher Sir Isaac Newton (1642–1721) published his great work, the *Principia Mathematica* (complete title, *Philosophiae Naturalis Principia Mathematica*, "The Natural

Philosophy of Mathematical Principles"), which not only included the law of gravitation but a theory of artificial satellites as well, even though his contemporaries did not realize the fact. The same work also contains what has come to be called Newton's third law of motion, which explains why a rocket works regardless of its surroundings—for example, when it is in empty space. Many other astronomers, mathematicians, and scientists made contributions during this first era of astronautical foundation laying: some by the discovery of additional bodies in the solar system, some by inventing and refining mathematical techniques for calculating orbits, some by discovering important laws of nature in other fields such as electromagnetics or chemistry.

By the year 1900 most of the fundamental facts of astronautics were known, though engineering techniques still had to be developed. It seems logical, then, that the theory of astronautics should have been formulated about then, so the period from 1900 to 1925 became a second era. Just before the turn of the century two men, one German, the other Russian, began to speculate about the possibility of building a spaceship.

The German, Hermann Ganswindt (1856–1934) spent his life on inventions, although he studied law originally. His space-travel plans never progressed beyond a sketch of his ship and an outline of how it was to work, but this was taken seriously enough to be criticized in detail by the Polish scientist Dr. Román, Baron von Gostkowski, Professor of Engineering at the University of Lemberg, in the Viennese journal *Die Zeit* ("The Time") in 1900. Dr. von Gostkowski pointed out that Ganswindt's high explosives could, at best, lift his ship to an altitude of about 30 miles. The Russian, Konstantin Eduardovitch Ziolkovsky (1857–1935), a teacher of physics and mathematics, in an article printed in *Na-ootch noye Obosreniye* ("Science Survey") in 1903 advanced the idea of large rockets for space travel. He suggested that liquid fuels be used in such rockets and pointed out that kerosene was a promising possibility. Actually, many large missiles today do burn kerosene; some still use alcohol, others, dimethyl hydrazine.

The theoretical work upon which today's astronautical activities are based was carried out, more or less simultaneously, by three men of different nationalities who at first did not know of one another's existence. Considered in the order in which these men wrote—not the order of their publication—the German engineer Dr. Walter Hohmann (1880–1944) must be mentioned first. About 1912 he, knowing that a rocket-propelled vehicle could accelerate or decelerate in empty space, began to wonder how such a vessel might travel from one planet to another, the problem being neither the airlessness of space nor the distances involved but the fundamental and often overlooked fact that all planets are in steady motion. Travel from the earth to Venus, for example, meant a take off from one moving platform and a landing on another. Dr. Hohmann began to note the problem's solutions and his calculations in 1914. In 1916 he put the finished manuscript aside; World War I was in progress and there was no hope of having it published. He revised it in 1924, and it was published under the title *Die Erreichbarkeit der Himmelskörper* ("The Attainability of the Heavenly Bodies").* The book contains only calculations of orbits and of fuel consumption; no engineering solutions are given.

The other two, the American Dr. Robert H. Goddard (1882–1945) and the Austrian professor Hermann Oberth wrote their works at about the same time, namely during the last years of World War I. Dr. Goddard's book, entitled *A Method of Reaching Extreme Altitudes,*† contains results of measurements on the exhaust velocity of various types of smokeless powder, calculations concerning rocket theory, and, in an appendix, a calculation of a shot to the moon. But Dr. Goddard's main aim was the creation of instrument-carrying rockets for the exploration of the upper atmosphere.

Hermann Oberth's work, *Die Rakete zu den Planetenräumen* ("The Rocket into Interplanetary Space")‡ advocated the use of liquid fuels, explained the step rocket (Goddard had done that too), and described in some detail the design of two

---

* Published by R. Oldenbourg, Munich, 1925.
† Published by the Smithsonian Institution, Washington, D.C. The title page bears the year 1919; actual distribution was in January 1920.
‡ Published by R. Oldenbourg, Munich, 1923.

rockets: one, Model B, an instrument-carrying rocket for the exploration of the upper atmosphere; the other, Model E, a man-carrying spaceship. Among the topics first mentioned by Oberth were: take off from water (the Navy's current Project Hydra); making the fuel tanks of a rocket out of sheet metal so thin that the tank would need pressurization even to maintain its shape (carried out in the Atlas rocket).

From 1900 to 1925, then, the fundamental books on rocket theory were written and published; the era of early experimentation came next. It began with Dr. Goddard's liquid-fuel rocket, fired for the first time from Auburn, Massachusetts, on March 16, 1926. By 1929 Oberth began to experiment; his work was carried on in Germany by the *Verein für Raumschiffahrt* (Society for Space Travel), and the first flights of liquid-fuel rockets in Europe took place in Germany in spring, 1931. Later that year, a Russian group began experimenting, and the first flight of a Russian liquid-fuel rocket was in spring, 1932. At about the same time, the German army became interested in rocket research and founded a rocket-research section headed by Captain (later General) Walter Dornberger, the eminent rocket engineer who was then a student in Berlin, with the young Wernher von Braun, as head of experimental work.

It was one of those accidents of history that the other experimenters dropped out one by one. There had been three experimenting groups in Germany: those of the engineers Johannes Winkler (1897–1947), Reinhold Tiling (1895?–1933?), and the Society for Space Travel. Winkler was requested to stop his experiments by his employer, the Junkers Aircraft Company; Reinhold Tiling, who worked with solid fuels, died in a laboratory explosion; and the Society for Space Travel was dissolved in 1933. The Russian group halted experiments in 1939, as did Dr. Goddard, for the simple but compelling reason that funds ran out. Hence the only working group left was that of the German army, which, after a number of preliminary models, developed the model A-4, later known as the famous V-2 rocket of World War II. The A-4 made its first successful flight on October 3, 1942, over a distance of 118 miles.

About a year later, the rocket was put into mass production, and on September 6, 1944, it was used as a weapon for the first time. Six months later, Nazi Germany collapsed, and the Research and Planning Staff of the German army's rocket research organization surrendered to the American Third Army; the production plant in the Harz Mountains was also occupied by American troops.

This was the beginning of the current era in the history of astronautics. All the preliminary work had been done; the first large rocket had not only been built, it had been mass produced, about 1,500 having been used operationally.

Systematic planning for the exploration of the upper atmosphere and the subsequent conquest of space was now possible. The planning was organized somewhat differently by the two main participants in the space age. The Russians had obtained only two complete V-2 rockets (earmarked for crew training) and, of course, all the manuals; their first step was, therefore, to build copies of the rockets in order to acquire practice. The United States had acquired (by taking possession of the underground plant in the Harz Mountains) about 75 unassembled rockets, and therefore never needed to build any of that type. Beginning in 1946, these devices were all fired in the so-called V-2 program, which involved shooting instrument-laden rockets into the upper atmosphere at the rate of about two a month.

Ten years after the collapse of Germany both the United States and the Soviet Union had progressed to the point where each country had an artificial-satellite program. The first actual project known was the 1954 joint Army-Navy project called Project Orbiter. Unfortunately, Project Orbiter was shelved in 1955 in favor of Project Vanguard. Late in 1955, the Russians stated that they were engaged in satellite studies, too. Somewhat later, both countries announced firing dates for the latter part of 1957.

The first Russian artificial satellite, Sputnik I, went into orbit on October 4, 1957; Sputnik II followed on November 3; Sputnik III was not orbited until May 15, 1958. The first American satellite, Explorer I, achieved orbit on January 31, 1958; the second American satellite, Vanguard I, followed on March 17; the third, Explorer III (Explorer II did not achieve orbit), on March 26.

The total number of successfully orbited satellites during the first four years of the space age was:

1957	2	(both Russian)
1958	6	(5 American, 1 Russian)
1959	11	(10 American, 1 Russian)
1960	19	(16 American, 3 Russian)

By the middle of 1962 the total number successfully orbited was close to 100, about a quarter of which were Russian, the others American, and one "international"—the satellite Ariel, built by the British and launched from Cape Canaveral by an American-built rocket on April 26, 1962.

To recapitulate, the scientific groundwork of astronautics had been laid in the centuries between 1600 and 1925; then the engineering development began. But with the engineering development an additional problem arose, that of organization. In the case of pre-Hitler and Hitler Germany the problem was relatively simple: the development was handled by the armed forces. In theory, each of the three services, Army, Navy, and Air Force, could have handled the program; in reality, the Army and Air Force came to an agreement: the Army handled the true rockets (for instance, the V-2) while the Air Force handled nonballistic applications of the reaction principle (for instance, the V-1 or buzz bomb). The German Navy did maintain a separate, though very small, establishment for research on naval applications of rockets.

In Russia space research is carried out by the USSR Academy of Sciences (*Akademus Hayk*) in collaboration with the Red Army, though details of the collaboration are not known.

In the United States some experimentation with missiles by the three armed services existed during World War II. Each service established departments for this purpose: that of the Air Force was known as PAD, standing for Pilotless Aircraft Division; the German V-2 rockets taken after World War II were handled by Army Ordnance; the first large American-built liquid-fuel rocket program, the Viking program, was a Navy project. While the Army established the White Sands

Proving Ground in New Mexico, the Navy's missile range was at Point Mugu in California, and the Air Force range was established at Cape Canaveral, Florida. The Vanguard program of the International Geophysical Year (IGY, which began in 1957) was officially under the supervision of the National Academy of Science, but was carried out primarily by persons who had been involved in the Viking program.

As time went on and the need for a nonmilitary agency became apparent, many proposals for its formation were made. In April 1958, Congress received a presidential message calling for a space agency, and early in August 1958 the agency was formed. Actually, an existing agency was given new scope. The National Advisory Committee on Aeronautics (NACA) had existed since World War I. In 1958 it was transformed into the National Aeronautics and Space Administration (NASA), and the Administrator of NACA, Dr. Hugh L. Dryden, became Deputy Administrator of NASA. It is NASA that is in charge of all scientific space activities. Of course, there are also military space projects handled by the respective services.

As for the actual program, the division of work is as follows: The Army's White Sands Proving Ground serves mainly as a training center for Army missile men; no space shots are fired from there. All such shots were to be fired from the Air Force's Cape Canaveral Missile Test Center, renamed the Atlantic Missile Range. The Air Force still operates this base and Vandenberg Air Force Base in California, which is a training center for personnel using well-proved missiles. Cape Canaveral, on the other hand, is a center where, in addition to the space shots, new and untried missiles are tested. After some experiments it became apparent that orbital shots to go over the poles could not be made from Cape Canaveral. If one attempted to fire northward from the Cape the first stage might fall on land—specifically, the coastal areas of Georgia. If one attempted to fire southward, the first stage could easily fall on Cuba, causing international incidents. Therefore, the shots into polar orbits had to be fired from California, where, after crossing the coastline on a southbound shot, no land is underneath the satellite until Antarctica is reached. Point Arguello, California, therefore became the Pacific Missile Range. Wallops Island, off the coast of Virginia, is used by NASA for vertical shots, such as upper-atmosphere soundings.

There are innumerable government reports on space activities, many of them in the nature of cost accounting. The most informative are those prepared for the use of members of Congress and for the public in general, giving detailed explanations of certain aspects of the space program.

The reports selected for this volume concern such useful satellite systems as can be expected to be working—thereby paying back some of our investment in space—within the next few years. The sequence of the discussions is based on the editor's personal guess as to when these systems will be fully operational. It seems likely that the navigational satellites will come first, the weather-service satellites next; the communication satellites (meaning those doing daily and nightly jobs, not the experimental types) will be the third system of useful satellites. Moreover, the civilian applications of these 3 satellite areas are perhaps the most important. Problems that could not have been solved without satellites are now being handled. It is for this reason that the historical and technical background of these areas is presented in considerable detail, and chronologies of the important events in the developments of meteorological and communication satellites, the most active of the three, are given in the Appendix.

Satellites for purely scientific research, such as astronomical observatories in orbit, have been touched on more sketchily, while such projects of the somewhat distant future as the astronomical observatory on the moon receive only casual mention. The reason is that the precise shape these projects will take is not, and cannot yet, be known. Their shape and scope will depend to some extent on information still to be gathered and instrumentation still to be developed.

WILLY LEY

Note on the Text

THIS BOOK is based, in the main, on the following publications of the United States Government:

Communication Satellites: Technical, Economic, and International Developments
Meteorological Satellites
Space Handbook: Astronautics and its Applications
Proposed Studies on the Implications of Peaceful Space Activities for Human Affairs
The Practical Values of Space Exploration

The material quoted is printed in larger text type, and after each quotation the source is given in a footnote. The editor's comments are set off from the text in a smaller size type; within the quoted material they are bracketed. All numbered references are from the original quoted material; other footnotes, asterisked, are the editor's.

Harnessing Space

1

㎭ㅤThe Means:
㎭ㅤOrbits and Rockets

A SURVEY of the underlying scientific facts is useful as the first step in a discussion of the process of orbiting a rocket. The discussion of the reasons for orbiting a device will be treated in a later chapter.

The nature of an orbit was explained correctly for the first time by Sir Isaac Newton in his *Principia Mathematica* in 1687 (First Book, Definition V):[*]

> A projectile, if it was not for the force of gravity, would not deviate towards the earth, but would go off from it in a right line, and that with a uniform motion, if the resistance of the air was taken away. It is by its gravity that it is drawn aside continually from its rectilinear course, and made to deviate towards the earth, more or less, according to the force of its gravity, and the velocity of its motion. The less its gravity is, or the quantity of its matter, or the greater the velocity with which it is projected, the less will it deviate from a rectilinear course, and the farther it will go. If a leaden ball, projected from the top of a mountain by the force of gunpowder, with a given velocity, and in

---

[*] Newton, Isaac (translated by Andrew Motte [1729], revised by Florian Cajon), *Principia in Modern English*, Berkeley, California, University of California Press, 1946.

a direction parallel to the horizon, is carried in a curved line to the distance of two miles before it falls to the ground; the same, if the resistance of the air were taken away, with a double or decuple [tenfold] velocity, would fly twice or ten times as far. And by increasing the velocity, we may at pleasure increase the distance to which it might be projected, and diminish the curvature of the line which it might describe, till at last it should fall at the distance of 10, 30, or 90 degrees, or might even go quite round the whole earth before it falls; or lastly, so that it might never fall to the earth, but go forwards into the celestial spaces, and proceed in its motion *in infinitum*. And after the same manner that a projectile, by the force of gravity, may be made to revolve in an orbit, and go round the whole earth, the moon also, either by the force of gravity, if it is endowed with gravity, or by any other force, that impels it towards the earth, may be continually drawn aside towards the earth, out of the rectilinear way which by its innate force it would pursue; and would be made to revolve in the orbit which it now describes. . . .

The prescription for producing an orbit around the earth, as contained in this "definition" of Sir Isaac Newton, contains three elements:

1. There must be no air resistance; for practical purposes this means a minimum distance from the earth greater than, say, 150 miles.

2. The impulse (push) for the orbiting body must be parallel to the ground.

3. The velocity must be sufficiently great; to give a few approximate modern figures: at a distance of 1,000 miles from sea level the velocity would have to be 4.4 miles per second, at a distance of 4,000 miles from sea level it would have to be 3.5

miles per second; and at a distance of 7,700 miles from sea level it would have to be 2.9 miles per second.

As regards the shape of an orbit, it is normally a closed curve, namely, an *ellipse*. A circle that, from the mathematical point of view, is only a special kind of an ellipse (namely, one in which the two focal points coincide) is a theoretical possibility, but it is most unlikely that such an orbit will actually occur. When space scientists speak of "circular orbits" they mean an ellipse that does not deviate much from a circle; they do not have a mathematical circle in mind. If the orbit is an open curve it is a *hyperbola*.

ꊾ   Space Terminology

Lay readers are sometimes confused when hearing the word *trajectory* used in connection with space operations.

The terms *trajectory* and *orbit* both refer to the path of a body in space. *Trajectory* is commonly used in connection with projectiles and is often associated with paths of limited extent, that is, paths having clearly identified initial and end points. *Orbit* is commonly used in connection with natural bodies (planets, moons, and so forth) and is often associated with paths that are more or less indefinitely extended or of a repetitive character, like the *orbit* of the moon around the earth. In discussions of space flight, both terms are used, with the choice usually dependent upon the nature of the flight path. Thus we speak of *trajectories* from the earth to the moon, and of satellite *orbits* around the earth.

The basic types of paths in space are determined by the gravitational-attraction properties of concentrated masses of material and the laws of motion discovered by Newton.

Virtually all major members of the solar system are approximately spherical in shape; and a spherical body will produce a force of attraction precisely like that of a single mass point located at the center of the body. Therefore, the fundamental problem is that of motion under the gravitational influence of a mass concentrated at a point.

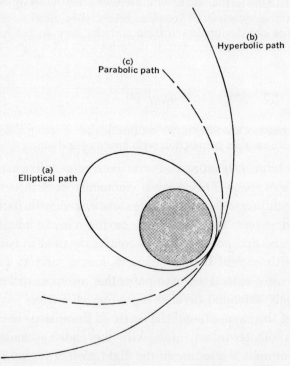

(b)
Hyperbolic path

(c)
Parabolic path

(a)
Elliptical path

Types of orbital paths.

In the figure above, (a) is an *elliptical orbit*—the familiar artificial-earth-satellite kind of orbit; (b) is a *hyperbolic orbit*—the kind that will characterize the start of an interplanetary flight. The elliptical orbit is closed on itself and would be traversed repetitively. The hyperbolic orbit is open, extending to infinity. Separating these two cases is a special one—the *parabolic orbit* (c)—similar in general appearance to the hyperbolic. The parabolic orbit is the borderline case between open and closed orbits and therefore identifies the borderline condition between space vehicles that are tied to paths (elliptical) in the general vicinity of their parent planet and those that can take up paths (hyperbolic) extending to regions remote from their parent planet. For any of these orbits the vehicle's velocity will be greatest at the point of nearest approach to the parent body, and it will be progressively less at more remote points.

The type of path that will be taken up by an unpowered space vehicle starting at a given location will depend upon its velocity. It will take up an open-ended path if its velocity equals or exceeds *escape velocity*; escape velocity is, by definition, that velocity required at a given location to establish a parabolic orbit. Velocities greater than escape velocity result in hyperbolic orbits. Lower velocities result in closed elliptical orbits—the vehicle is tied to the neighborhood of the planet.

Since it essentially separates "local" from "long-distance" flights, escape velocity is clearly a primary astronautical parameter. The exact value of this velocity is dependent upon two factors: (a) the mass of the parent planet, and (b) the distance from the center of the planet to the space vehicle. Escape velocity increases as the square root of the planet's mass, and decreases as the square root of the distance from the planet's center. The speeds required for escape directly from the surfaces of various bodies of interest are listed in Table 1. These escape-velocity requirements are a measure of the difficulty of departure from these bodies.

Table 1
SURFACE ESCAPE VELOCITY

	Feet per second
Mercury	13,600
Venus	33,600
Earth	36,700
Moon	7,800
Mars	16,700
Asteroid Eros	50
Jupiter	197,000

The projection speed required to escape directly from the earth's surface is about 36,700 feet per second. If a vehicle takes up unpowered flight (end of rocket propulsion) at an altitude of, say, 300 miles, it requires the somewhat lesser speed of 35,400 feet per second to escape into interplanetary space. This reduction in required velocity has, of course, been obtained at the expense of the energy expended in lifting the vehicle to an altitude of 300 miles.

The elliptical orbits generated by velocities below escape velocity are the type followed by artificial satellites, as well as by all the planets and moons of the solar system.

The period of the satellite—the time required to make one full circuit—is dependent upon the mass of the parent body and the distance across the orbit at its greatest width (the length of the *major axis*). The period is less if the parent body is more massive—the earth's moon moves more slowly than similarly placed moons of Jupiter. The period gets longer as the length of the major axis increases—the period of the moon, with a major axis of about 500,000 miles, is much longer than those of the first artificial satellites, with major axes of about 9,000 miles.

The velocity required to establish a satellite at an altitude of a few hundred miles above the earth is about 25,000 feet per second. This required *orbital velocity* is less at greater altitudes. At the distance of the moon it is only about 3,300 feet per second.

Once a vehicle is in space, moving at high velocity, say in a satellite orbit, it requires no further propulsion to stay aloft. Its flight path can, however, be very appreciably influenced and great increases in velocity imparted by very small forces acting over long periods of time. The fact that useful results can be derived from small thrusts in space—thrusts that would be entirely insignificant on the earth—leads to interest in unique propulsion systems based on electrical-accelerator principles. One kind of application of particular interest involves use of heavy conventional propulsion systems to develop orbital velocity (say, 25,000 feet per second) and then to build up the remaining 12,000 feet per second to reach escape velocity by a low-thrust electrical system.[1,2]

To execute a flight to one of the other planets, a vehicle must first escape from the earth. Achievement of escape velocity, however, is only part of the problem; other factors must be considered, particularly the sun's gravitational field and the motion of the earth about the sun.

Before launching, the vehicle is at the earth's distance

from the sun, moving with the earth's speed around the sun—about 100,000 feet per second. Launching at greater than earth escape velocity results in the vehicle's taking up an independent orbit around the sun at a velocity some-

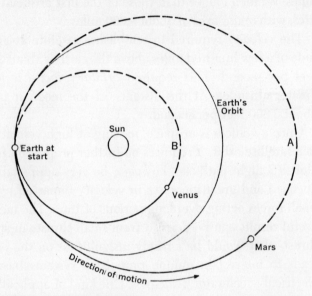

Interplanetary trajectories.

what different from that of the earth. If it is fired in the same direction as the earth's orbital motion, it will have an independent velocity around the sun greater than that of the earth. It will then take up an orbit like A, in the above figure, which moves farther from the sun than the earth's orbit; the vehicle could, if properly launched, reach the outer planets, Mars, Jupiter, and so forth. The minimum launch velocities required to reach these planets are given in Table 2.

Table 2

MINIMUM LAUNCH VELOCITIES, WITH TRANSIT TIMES, TO REACH ALL PLANETS

	Minimum launching velocity (FEET PER SECOND)	*Transit time*
Mercury	44,000	110 days
Venus	38,000	150 days
Mars	38,000	260 days
Jupiter	46,000	2.7 years
Saturn	49,000	6 years
Uranus	51,000	16 years
Neptune	52,000	31 years
Pluto	53,000	46 years

The velocities in Table 2 are minimum requirements, and lead to flight times as shown. Higher velocities will reduce flight times.

If the vehicle is launched "backward," or against the earth's velocity, it will assume an independent velocity less than that of the earth and move on an orbit like B (opposite), so that it could reach the inner planets Venus and Mercury.

To reach the more distant portions of the solar system requires that the vehicle take up a velocity, relative to the sun, that is considerably *greater* than that of the earth. A large launch velocity is required to produce this excess (after a good deal of it has been absorbed by the earth's gravitational field). On the other hand, to travel in close to the sun requires that the vehicle take up a velocity, relative to the sun, that is considerably *less* than that of the earth. A large launch velocity is this time required to cancel out the component of vehicle velocity due to the earth's motion, and again much of the launch velocity is absorbed by the earth's gravitational field. Thus, as seen from Table 2, it is almost as hard to propel a vehicle in to Mercury as it is to propel it out to Jupiter.*

ㅿ The Take Off

All these various possibilities are taken into account in current official planning, which comprises artificial satellites, both manned and unmanned, in orbits around the earth, manned flight around the moon, and finally a landing on the moon and unmanned space probes to both Venus and Mars. The Venus and Mars probes will travel along connecting orbits without extra power (except such as might be needed for mid-course guidance and corrections). Plans for a Jupiter probe, however, include constant acceleration by means of an *ion drive* (an electrical propulsion system) after the probe has been placed into an orbit around the earth by means of a chemical rocket.

As the foregoing discussion has shown, the lowest useful velocity is 4½ to 5 miles per second. And of all the devices known to engineering, only the rocket is capable of attaining such velocities. The proverbial "speed of a cannonball" is far too low, since even the long and heavy guns of battleships never imparted a higher muzzle velocity to their shells than about ½ mile per second. The rocket can attain these high velocities precisely because it does not depend on a single impulse, like

* From *Space Handbook: Astronautics and its Applications;* Staff Report of the Select Committee on Astronautics and Space Exploration, Washington, D.C., 1959, pp. 19–23.

an artillery shell, but is subjected to a steady acceleration lasting as long as the rocket engine is operating.

A rocket may be described as the reverse of a gun. In a gun the gases produced by the explosion of a gunpowder-like mixture impart speed to the bullet. That the firing is accompanied by a recoil is considered a nuisance that cannot be helped. It is, for our discussion here, important to keep in mind that recoil also occurs when blank cartridges are fired. The powder gases hurtling from the muzzle, then, do produce a recoil even if they do not carry a bullet. In firing a rocket it is this recoil that is important; this is the thrust that carries the rocket upward. The rocket engine producing the stream of fire, and with it the thrust, naturally needs fuel, which has to be stored somewhere. Finally, there has to be a reason for the shot; the purpose may be to carry a warhead to a distant point on the earth or to place an instrument package into orbit.

Keeping these fundamentals in mind, we see why a rocket consists of three main components. One is the load, which is determined by the purpose of the shot and is called the *payload;* the second is the rocket engine used to propel the whole apparatus; and the third is the structure holding payload and engine in place as well as tanks containing the rocket fuel. This structure has come to be called the *airframe*, mainly because manufacturers of rockets usually began as manufacturers of aircraft.

Vertical take off from the earth requires a thrust force that exceeds the weight of the complete missile by some 30 to 50 per cent (a thrust-to-weight ratio of 1.3 to 1.5). For easiest engine operation, the thrust produced during the entire propulsive period is usually constant, causing the vehicle to be accelerated at a progressively higher rate as the vehicle weight diminishes due to propellant consumption.

In rocket vehicles intended to reach velocities of interest in astronautics, the largest fraction of the missile weight is

(*Opposite*) Mariner II spacecraft poised for launching at Cape Canaveral. The payload is under the shroud at the top of the Atlas-Agena B rocket.

The payload of this rocket is the 28-inch canister containing a folded Echo satellite. The canister rests on a Thor-Able rocket.

devoted to the propellants, and the largest volume to the storage of these propellants.

The propellant tanks, and the supporting structure . . . (the airframe) [are] considered "dead weight," since the airframe does not contribute directly to the production of thrust or to the useful payload. Rather, the dead weight imposes a limitation on the maximum velocity that a given rocket can achieve—even with no payload.

Another factor contributing significantly to the total dead weight of a vehicle and restricting its maximum performance is any unused propellant trapped in the propulsion system (rocket engine, plumbing, and tanks) at thrust cutoff. In liquid-propellant rockets, two propellant fluids are stored in separate tanks, which should be emptied at very nearly the same instant. The engine will stop when either propellant is exhausted, and the remaining portion of the other propellant will be trapped as residual dead weight.

The flight velocities required for astronautics far exceed those obtainable with a single rocket unit using conventional propulsion techniques, regardless of the size of the rocket. The *multistage* rocket can provide adequate velocities, however. On this type of vehicle, one rocket (or more) is carried to high speed by another rocket, to be launched independently when the first rocket is exhausted. If, for example, the first stage reaches a terminal velocity of 10,000 feet per second and launches a second stage also capable of developing 10,000 feet per second, the net ter-

(*Opposite*) Take off of an Atlas rocket from Cape Canaveral.

minal velocity of the second stage will be 20,000 feet per second.

Staging can be extended to include 3,4, and more stages to develop higher velocities. The total velocity that may be attained is the sum of the individual contributions of each stage. A practical difficulty will generally restrict the number of stages that can be profitably employed, since the weight of structure required to connect the stages tends to increase dead weight and defeat the purpose of staging.

Control of the flight path of a rocket-propelled vehicle is achieved by altering the direction of engine thrust by one of a variety of methods, including swiveling the engine itself. Velocity control is provided through termination of all rocket thrust at the exact time the desired velocity is reached.*

⋈ Selecting Rocket Fuels

Before the various types of fuel in use can be discussed, one fundamental concept has to be explained. It is obvious that, if there are several kinds available, one of these fuels is likely to be more powerful than another. How does one rate a rocket fuel? The very performance of a rocket provides a handy system.

If you have one rocket burning old-fashioned black gunpowder and another burning the high-grade smokeless powder specifically developed for rocket flights, the exhaust velocities

* From *Space Handbook: Astronautics and its Applications, op. cit.,* pp. 27–28.

(*Opposite*) An Agena satellite being hoisted to be mated with an Atlas booster.

of the combustion gases from these two kinds of powder will be different. For example: the exhaust blast of the black gunpowder will move with a velocity of about 2,000 feet per second, relative to the rocket (and not to the ground). The exhaust blast of the smokeless powder will be approximately 5,500 feet per second. One measure of the power of the fuel, therefore, is in the exhaust velocity it produces. But, as rocket experimentation progressed, it was found practical to use a different figure—one reflecting the exhaust velocity rather than the exhaust velocity itself. This figure is called the *specific impulse*, or I_{sp}. The specific impulse is calculated by dividing the thrust of a given rocket by the amount of fuel consumed per second and is expressed in seconds.

If a rocket engine develops a thrust of 50,000 pounds and consumes 250 pounds of fuel per second, the fuel is said to have a specific impulse of $50,000 \div 250 = 200$. Twenty-five years ago, a specific impulse of 200 would have been considered something very nice indeed. Now, 200 is thought to be at the lower end of the scale of what is useful, and any rocket designer would pick a propellant producing a specific impulse of about 250, unless the 200-fuel is very cheap and the 250-fuel very expensive. A rocket fuel is therefore rated according to the specific impulse it is capable of delivering (see Table 3).

It can be seen from the following table that the chemical propellants in common use deliver specific impulse values ranging from about 175 up to about 300 seconds. The most energetic chemical propellants are theoretically capable of specific impulses up to about 400 seconds.

High values of specific impulse are obtained from high exhaust–gas temperature, and from exhaust gas having very low (molecular) weight. To be efficient, therefore, a propellant should have a large heat of combustion to yield high temperatures, and should produce combustion products containing simple, light molecules embodying such elements as hydrogen (the lightest), carbon, oxygen, fluorine, and the lighter metals (aluminum, beryllium, lithium).

Another important factor is the density of a propellant. A given weight of dense propellant can be carried in a smaller, lighter tank than the same weight of a low-density propellant. Liquid hydrogen, for example, is energetic and its combustion gases are light. However, it is a very bulky substance, requiring large tanks. The dead weight of these tanks partly offsets the high specific impulse of the hydrogen propellant.

Other criteria must also be considered in choosing propellants. Some chemicals that yield excellent specific impulse create problems in engine operation. Some are not adequate as coolants for the hot thrust-chamber walls. Others exhibit peculiarities in combustion that render their use difficult or impossible. Some are unstable to varying degrees and cannot be stored or handled safely. Such features inhibit their use for rocket propulsion.

The blast off of a Thor-Delta rocket carrying a Tiros satellite.

Table 3

SPECIFIC IMPULSE OF SOME TYPICAL CHEMICAL PROPELLANTS

Propellant combinations	I_{sp} *range (seconds)*
Monopropellants (liquid):	
Low-energy monopropellants	160 to 190
Hydrazine	
Ethylene oxide	
Hydrogen peroxide	
High-energy monopropellants	190 to 230
Nitromethane	
Bipropellants (liquid):	
Low-energy bipropellants	200 to 230
Perchloryl fluoride—Available fuel	
Aniline—Acid *	
JP-4—Acid *	
Hydrogen peroxide—JP-4	
Medium-energy bipropellants	230 to 260
Hydrazine—Acid	
Ammonia—Nitrogen tetroxide	
High-energy bipropellants	250 to 270
Liquid oxygen—JP-4 *	
Liquid oxygen—Alcohol *	
Hydrazine—Chlorine trifluoride	
Very high-energy bipropellants	270 to 330
Liquid oxygen and fluorine—JP-4	
Liquid oxygen and ozone—JP-4	
Liquid oxygen—Hydrazine	

* The fuels marked with an asterisk are those in regular use in rockets and missiles.

Propellant combinations	I_{sp} *range* (*seconds*)
Super high-energy bipropellants	300 to 385
Fluorine—Hydrogen	
Fluorine—Ammonia	
Ozone—Hydrogen	
Fluorine—Diborane	
Oxidizer-binder combinations (solid):	
Potassium perchlorate	
Thiokol or asphalt	170 to 210
Ammonium perchlorate	
Thiokol	170 to 210
Rubber	170 to 210
Polyurethane	210 to 250
Nitropolymer	210 to 250
Ammonium nitrate	
Polyester	170 to 210
Rubber	170 to 210
Nitropolymer	210 to 250
Double base	170 to 250
Boron metal components and oxidant	200 to 250
Lithium metal components and oxidant	200 to 250
Aluminum metal components and oxidant	200 to 250
Magnesium metal components and oxidant	200 to 250
Perfluoro-type propellants	250 and above

Unfortunately, almost any propellant that gives good performance is apt to be a very active chemical; hence, most propellants are corrosive, flammable, or toxic, and are often all three. One of the most tractable liquid propellants is gasoline. But while it is comparatively simple

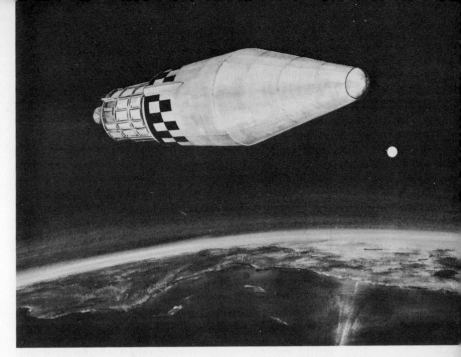

Drawing of a Discoverer satellite carried aloft by a Thor booster, in orbit around the earth.

to use, gasoline is, of course, highly flammable and must be handled with care. Many propellants are highly toxic, to a greater degree even than most war gases; some are so corrosive that only a few special substances can be used to contain them; some may burn spontaneously upon contact with air, or upon contacting any organic substance, or in certain cases upon contacting most common metals.

Also essential to the choice of a rocket propellant is its availability. In some cases, in order to obtain adequate

(*Opposite*) The main stage of an Atlas rocket as it separates from the nose cone about 200 miles above the Atlantic Ocean.

amounts of a propellant, an entirely new chemical plant must be built. And because some propellants are used in very large quantities, the availability of raw materials must be considered.

Most liquid chemical rockets use two separate propellants: a fuel and an oxidizer. Typical fuels include kerosene, alcohol, hydrazine and its derivatives, and liquid hydrogen. Many others have been tested and used. Oxidizers include nitric acid, nitrogen tetroxide, liquid oxygen, and liquid fluorine. Some of the best oxidizers are liquefied gases, such as oxygen and fluorine, which exist as liquids only at very low temperatures; this adds greatly to the difficulty of their use in rockets. Most fuels, with the exception of hydrogen, are liquids at ordinary temperatures.

Certain propellant combinations are *hypergolic*—that is, they ignite spontaneously upon contact of the fuel and oxidizer. Others require an igniter to start them burning, although they will continue to burn when injected into the flame of the combustion chamber.

In general, the liquid propellants in common use yield specific impulses superior to those of available solids. On the other hand, they require more complex engine systems to transfer the liquid propellants to the combustion chamber. A list showing solid- and liquid-propellant performances is given in Table 3 (pp. 48–49).

Liquid oxygen is the standard oxidizer used in the largest United States rocket engines. It is chemically stable and noncorrosive, but its extremely low temperature makes pumping, valving, and storage difficult. If placed in contact with organic materials, it will cause fire or an explosion.

Nitric acid and nitrogen tetroxide are common industrial

chemicals. Although they are corrosive to some substances, materials are available that will safely contain these fluids. Nitrogen tetroxide, since it boils at fairly low temperatures, must be protected to some degree.

Liquid fluorine is a very low-temperature substance, comparable with liquid oxygen, and is highly toxic and corrosive as well. Furthermore, its products of combustion are extremely corrosive and dangerous; hence, the use of fluorine raises problems in testing and operating rocket engines.

Most liquid fuels, with the exception of hydrogen, are closely alike in performance and handling. They are usually quite tractable substances. Hydrogen, however, exists as a liquid only at extremely low temperatures—lower even than liquid oxygen; hence, it is very difficult to handle and store. Also, if allowed to escape into the air, it can form a highly explosive mixture. It is a very bulky substance, about $\frac{1}{14}$ as dense as water. Nonetheless, it offers the best performance of any of the liquid fuels.

The use of more than two chemicals as propellants in rockets has never received a great deal of attention, and is not considered advantageous at present. Occasionally, a separate propellant is used to operate the gas generator that supplies the gas to drive the turbopumps of liquid rockets. In the V-2, for example, hydrogen peroxide was decomposed to supply the hot gas for the main turbopumps, although the main rocket propellants were alcohol and liquid oxygen.

Certain unstable, liquid chemicals that, under proper conditions, will decompose and release energy, have been tried as rocket propellants. Their performance, however, is inferior to that of bipropellants or modern solid propellants, and they are of most interest in rather specialized applications, like small control rockets. Outstanding examples of this type of propellants are hydrogen peroxide and ethylene oxide.*

The fuel and oxidizer are stored in the rocket in separate containers. How they are transported from the fuel tanks to the combustion chamber where they come together to burn depends on the over-all size of the rocket. If the rocket is comparatively small (say, an instrument carrier) with a take-off weight of not more than about 150 pounds, it is both possible and practical to pressurize the fuel tanks and to feed the two liquids into the rocket motor simply by pressure. Then, however, the tanks have to be strong enough to stand this pressure, which would be between 350 and 500 pounds per square inch. For large rockets, this increases the dead weight too much, and the propellants are forced into the rocket motor by high-pressure pumps; the tanks are pressurized only to the extent of enabling them to keep their shape when the fluid is drained from them rapidly.

In a solid-fuel rocket the case containing the fuel and the place where the fuel is burned are one and the same; hence the whole rocket case was referred to as the "rocket motor" in all World War II military rockets.

ᙡ Other Types of Propulsion

Two general types of solid propellants are in use. The first, the so-called double-base propellant, consists of nitrocellulose and nitroglycerine, plus additives in small quantity. There is no separate fuel and oxidizer. The molecules

* From *Space Handbook: Astronautics and its Applications, op. cit.,* pp. 42–45.

are unstable and upon ignition break apart and rearrange themselves, liberating large quantities of heat. These propellants lend themselves well to smaller rocket motors. They are often processed and formed by extrusion methods, although casting has also been employed.

The other type of solid propellant is the composite. Here, separate fuel and oxidizer chemicals are used, intimately mixed in the solid grain. The oxidizer is usually ammonium nitrate, potassium chlorate, or ammonium chlorate, and often comprises as much as $4/5$ or more of the whole propellant mix. The fuels used are hydrocarbons, such as asphaltic-type compounds, or plastics. Because the oxidizer has no significant structural strength, the fuel must not only perform well but must also supply the necessary form and rigidity to the grain. Much of the research in solid propellants is devoted to improving the physical as well as the chemical properties of the fuel.

Ordinarily, in processing solid propellants the fuel and oxidizer components are separately prepared for mixing, the oxidizer being a powder and the fuel a fluid of varying consistency. They are then blended together under carefully controlled conditions and poured into the prepared rocket case as a viscous semisolid. They are then caused to be set in curing chambers under controlled temperature and pressure.

Solid propellants offer the advantage of minimum maintenance and instant readiness. However, the more energetic solids may require carefully controlled storage conditions, and may offer handling problems in the very large sizes, since the rocket must always be carried about fully loaded. Protection from mechanical shocks or abrupt temperature changes that may crack the grain is essential.*

Two other types of propulsion—both rocket-like in that they develop thrust—must be mentioned. One of them is ion propulsion in which the "fuel" is a metal—cesium and mercury are most often mentioned. The molecules of the metallic fuel are then

caused to have an electric charge—that is, the propellant is ionized. This might be accomplished by passing the propellant over heated metal grids. It is then possible to accelerate the charged molecules, or ions, to very high velocities through a nozzle by means of an electric field. (Electrons are accelerated in a television picture tube in this fashion.) The performance of such an ion engine is very good, with values of specific impulse estimated to be as high as 20,000. However, the amount of electric power required is very large, so weight of the power-generating equipment becomes a major obstacle to an efficient vehicle. It is contemplated that some type of nuclear fission (or fusion, farther in the future) could be used to supply the energy for the electric power plant, although this step would still not eliminate the need for heavy electrical generators, unless direct conversion of fission to electrical energy in large quantities became practical.

For example, an ion rocket offering 20,000 seconds of specific impulse, using cesium for the propellant, would require about 2,100 kilowatts of electric power to produce 1 pound of thrust, assuming good efficiency. Optimistic

* From *Space Handbook: Astronautics and its Applications, op. cit.*, p. 43.

estimates of electric-power-supply weight indicate that the power unit would weigh about 8,500 pounds. The weight of the ion accelerator itself is small in comparison. Therefore, an ion rocket can accelerate itself only very slowly (in this example less than 1/10,000 of 1 g—the unit of gravity when motionless).

Ion propulsion holds promise for use in unmanned probes to be sent to distant planets, but it will not be used for satellites. The other is the atomic rocket, which is being developed as part of a larger atomic research project called Project Rover. The nuclear rocket must carry a liquid of some kind as the propellant, which produces the exhaust. This "working fluid," as it has also been called, is likely to be a chemical,

although no energy is supplied to the rocket by any chemical reaction. All the heat comes from the reactor. Since the prime consideration is to minimize the molecular weight of the exhaust gas, liquid hydrogen is the best substance so far considered, and it does not seem likely that any substance with superior performance can be found. The problems of handling liquid hydrogen are the same for the nuclear rocket as for the chemical rocket.

Another substance mentioned for use as a propellant in the nuclear rocket is ammonia. While offering only about ½ the specific impulse of hydrogen for the same reactor temperature as a consequence of its greater molecular weight, it is a liquid at reasonable temperatures and is easily handled. Its density is also much greater than hydrogen, being about the same as that of gasoline.[*]

[*] From *Space Handbook: Astronautics and its Applications, op. cit.,* pp. 45–46.

The equivalent of the specific impulse expected from the nuclear rocket is about 330, which means that it could compete with very high-energy, and therefore very "touchy"—that is, unstable—chemical propellants. Once developed, the nuclear rocket should be a much safer device than rockets using these difficult chemicals.

But even the relatively simple chemical now being burned in our large rockets, a kerosenelike fuel with liquid oxygen, are good enough for all satellite applications of the foreseeable future.

REFERENCES

1. Boden, R. H., *The Ion Rocket Engine,* North American Aviation, Rocketdyne Division, Rept. No. R-645, August 26, 1957.

2. Stublinger, E., *Space Travel with Electric Propulsion Systems,* Army Ballistic Missile Agency, November 11, 1958.

3. "Some Considerations Pertaining to Space Navigation," Aerojet-General Corporation, Special Report No. 1450, May 1958. (Reprinted in *Communication Satellites: Technical, Economic, and International Developments;* Staff Report prepared for the use of the Committee on Aeronautical and Space Sciences, United States Senate (87th Congress, 2d Session), February 25, 1962.

2 Artificial Satellites as Navigational Aids

SINCE the first suggestion for an artificial satellite in scientific literature (in Hermann Oberth's first book in 1923) was written in 1920 and 1921, when radio was a novelty and the realm of shortwave transmission unexplored, it is not at all surprising that none of the uses now under discussion was mentioned. Oberth's suggestion was to build a large spaceship equipped with a "landing boat" and to leave the ship in orbit around the earth while the pilot returned to the ground by means of the landing boat. Additional loads were to be brought up in the same manner and put together to form the kind of structure later called a space station. Since it was then believed that radio waves could not penetrate the ionized region then called the Kennelly-Heaviside layer,* Oberth also had to assume that communication between the space station and the ground had to be by light signals. He did think that the space station might be able to warn ships in an iceberg area, but it did not occur to him that the space station, once in a well-established orbit, could be a navigational aid by itself.

The easy visibility of the first communication satellite Echo I, intended to test the feasibility of passive communication satellites (see pp. 131–133), has demonstrated, however, that a large space station could have value for this purpose.

Though most of the publications, both professional and pop-

* Edwin Kennelly (1861–1939) and Oliver Heaviside (1850–1925) were two pioneers in radio-wave propagation who independently postulated a reflecting layer in 1902, later named after them.

ular, of the last six years have dealt with comparatively small and unmanned artificial satellites for specific purposes, the idea of the large, manned space station has not been discarded by scientists and industry. The advantage of a large space station with trained personnel aboard is that it could do so many different things. Originally, it had been conceived as a reconnaissance vehicle, with the main purpose of watching for suspicious moves of potential enemies and the secondary purpose of maintaining a continuous charting of air-mass movements for meteorological purposes. It followed automatically that the space station could also replace the International Iceberg Patrol (founded as a result of the *Titanic* disaster in 1912) and check on the location of expeditions. That it was also to be utilized as an astronomical observatory and a research station goes without saying.

But practical navigators realized later (after World War II) that such a station would also be a navigational device. It could be seen easily after dusk and before dawn; and it could be made visible during the day by means of a reflecting mirror diverting sunlight toward the earth and in the midnight sky by means of a searchlight aimed at the earth. It now would be quite easy to increase its usefulness by making it "visible" by radio for areas covered by a cloud layer.

However, since 1959 work by the Navy on small specialized navigational satellites, called Project Transit, has continued, and there can be no doubt that such satellites will be in operation before a large space station is attempted.

ꊼ Satellites as Reference Points

Artificial satellites can provide the basis for all-weather, long-term navigation systems to determine with accuracy geodetic position, speed, and direction of a surface vehicle or aircraft, north reference [direction to the star Polaris], and vertical reference [at right angles to the north reference]. Other methods, such as dead reckoning [establishing approximate position from the ship's log], sun and star

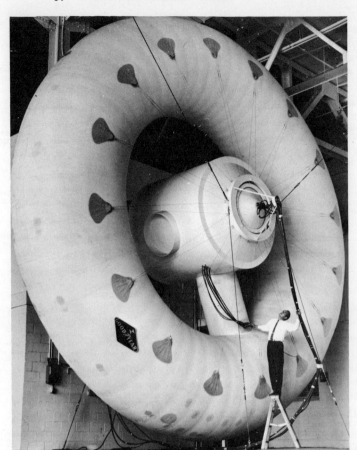

Research model of an inflatable space station designed
and built by the Goodyear Aircraft Corporation.

sighting during clear weather, and use of inertial guidance
devices [a special application of gyroscopes] can provide
such information with adequate precision in many applications for limited periods of time. It is, however, necessary

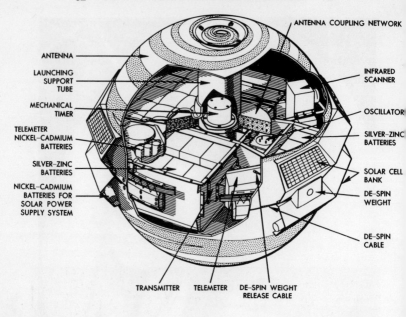

Cut-away drawing of Transit I showing its internal mechanism.

in many cases to check, independently and periodically, the navigation data indicated by these systems.

In checking and correcting navigational data, two distinct techniques employing a satellite are of interest: (1) sphereographical navigation, which is very similar to celestial navigation, and (2) a method making use of the Doppler-shift phenomenon.[1-4]

Celestial guidance involves measurement of the angle between the vertical and the line of sight to a celestial body. The position of the observer on the earth's surface can be determined from . . . observations of two celestial bodies. The same kind of procedure can be used to determine position from two successive observations of a satellite. There are, of course, differences in detail between navigation by stars and by satellite, since star positions change very slowly while a satellite fairly close to the earth moves at great speed. In both applications the observer must also determine the local direction of the vertical by pendulum or some other device.

For all-weather navigation, the satellite would radiate a continuous radio signal. The observer equipped with an electronic sextant [an instrument for measuring angles

Transit IB before being fitted to its rocket. The painted stripes indicate the antenna.

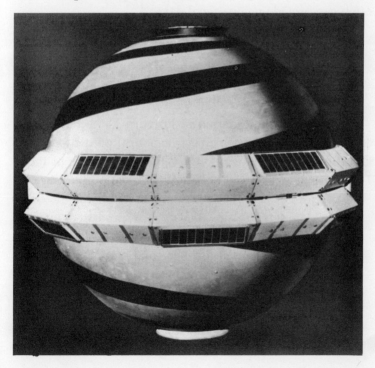

electrically instead of visually] and an indicator of the vertical would then be able to determine his position from radio observations of the satellite.

An all-weather navigation system can also be based on a satellite broadcasting a continuous radio signal, by using the Doppler-shift principle. The basic phenomenon is the following: The radio signal received from a moving vehicle will appear higher in frequency as the vehicle approaches the observer and lower as the vehicle recedes from the observer. The difference between the observed signal frequency and the known transmitter frequency is a measure of relative position and motion of the vehicle and observer; and, therefore, proper use of such frequency-shift information can provide navigational data.

This type of system does not require determination of the local vertical by the observer.

For either of the above methods, the observer must know the true position of the satellite at the time of observation. Thus, he must be provided with a table of satellite positions covering the duration of his trip. These tables must be prepared in advance as mathematical predictions, as is now done by the Naval Observatory in the case of tables of positions of celestial bodies for navigation purposes.

Navigation accuracy is dependent upon the precision with which satellite position can be predicted into the future. This precision is, in turn, dependent largely upon the accuracy of observations, the computational procedure used, the accuracy with which the relevant physical constants are known, and the magnitudes of unpredictable disturbing effects acting on the satellite. The most important of these disturbances is the uncertain air drag at lower altitudes. Since it is at fairly high altitudes, the orbit of

Vanguard I can be predicted into the future for about a month with reasonable accuracy, whereas predictions of the lower Explorer IV orbit are useful for only about one day in the future. Current predictions of Vanguard I position tend to be in error by some tens of miles after a month, but are in error by less than 5 miles over a few days. Prediction a few hours in advance would be off by less than a mile.

In addition to errors in satellite observations, there are two sources of difficulty in accurate orbit predictions. First, the classical methods used for many years by astronomers to determine orbits have not proved to be adequate when used in connection with artificial-satellite orbits. New techniques or modifications of existing techniques appear to be necessary in order to improve the accuracy of orbital predictions. Second, further study must be made of the disturbing forces influencing orbital motion.

The basic measurements required in a sphereographical navigation are the azimuth and elevation angles of the satellite and the time of observation. The equipment of the navigator consists of a highly directional antenna and receiver, a clock, and equipment for defining the vertical. The accuracy of navigation is determined by various equipment characteristics. The factor with greatest implications for vehicle design is the antenna size.

As an indication of this size, an antenna about 12 feet in diameter will allow position determination within an error of about a mile when directed toward a satellite 1,000 miles away under representative conditions. A smaller antenna would lead to larger errors. The other equipments involved are generally comparatively small and light. The satellite would carry a transmitter.

Drawing of Transit IIA and a separate satellite carried "piggyback"; when released by spring force, it travels in its own orbit.

When using the Doppler technique of navigation the physical extent of the equipment needed on the navigated vehicle is less. The navigation equipment consists of a sensitive radio receiver, an accurate frequency reference, and an accurate clock. The equipment carried by the satellite would again be a transmitter, but one specifically designed to emit a very stable frequency.*

* From *Space Handbook: Astronautics and its Applications;* Staff Report of the Select Committee on Astronautics and Space Exploration, Washington, D.C., 1959, pp. 199–201.

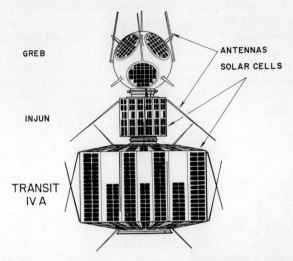

Drawing of Transit IVA and 2 "piggyback" satellites, Injun and Greb. The 3 satellites separate and follow their own orbits.

Experimental navigational satellites that have been launched are the following:

Table 4

PROTOTYPES OF NAVIGATIONAL SATELLITES

Designation	Date of Launching	First Perigee* (MILES)	First Apogee† (MILES)	Orbital Period (MINUTES)	Weight of Satellite (POUNDS)	Remarks
Transit I B	Apr. 13 '60	239	472	95.9	265	
Transit II A	June 22 '60	389	658	102	265	orbiting
Transit III B	Feb. 22 '61	117	429	93.2	250	
Transit IV A	June 29 '61	547	620	103.8	not ann.	orbiting

* Point of orbit closest to the earth.
† Point of orbit farthest from the earth.

It is possible that some of the classified satellites launched during the first part of 1962 might have contained navigational components. Though it has been announced that the navigational satellites will be made available to navigators of all nations, it must be kept in mind that such satellites would be of special value to nuclear-powered submarines on long cruises that might wish to check their own guidance equipment with the satellite position indication. Exactly how often such satellites have actually been used for navigation purposes has not been revealed by the Navy.

REFERENCES

1. Lawrence, L., Jr., *Navigation by Satellites, Missiles and Rockets,* vol. 1, No. 1, October 1956, p. 48.

2. Siry, I. W., *The Vanguard IGY Earth Satellite Program,* Naval Research Laboratory, presented to the Fifth General Assembly of CSAGI. Held in Moscow July 30 to August 10, 1958.

3. Leighton, R. B., *Tracking an Artificial Satellite Using the Doppler Effect,* California Institute of Technology, October 28, 1957.

4. Quier, W. H., and Weiffenbach, G. C., *Theoretical Analysis of Doppler Radio Signals from Earth Satellites,* Johns Hopkins Applied Physics Laboratory, Bumblebee Series Report No. 276, April 1958.

3 Weather Research and Artificial Satellites

WEATHER is not only something about which nothing, or only very little, can be done, it has two other characteristics: it is an ever-changing condition, and it is truly international in character.

Consequently, meteorology, the science concerned with the weather, was the first subject of an international congress, in 1873, in Vienna. Of course scientists in other fields of learning had held meetings on a regional or national basis before that date. Individual scientists (zoologists, engineers, and others) in those days often traveled beyond the borders of their homeland to be guest speakers at scientific meetings in countries other than their own. But the meteorologists were the first to plan an international meeting, the First International Meteorological Congress, which Carl von Stremayr, Minister of Instruction of the Austro-Hungarian Empire, opened in Vienna on September 2, 1873.

His opening remarks ran as follows:

It is a fruitful thought to introduce to all countries, by the personal intercourse of and united action between men of science, a common system of observation, and a discussion of the meteorological phenomena which in their varying forms are manifested over the entire earth. In this way not only will scientific investigation more speedily reach its goal, but also that highly practical point of view will be sooner attained, which will direct on the progress of meteorology, the eyes, not only of sailors and agriculturists, but of all educated men.

Perhaps a most significant phrase is that in which he referred to "a common system of observation," for it is this above all that still provides the common ground for international cooperation.

And even today, the atmosphere providing the medium for the world's weather probably remains as the most truly international factor of life here on the earth. That this fact has long been recognized is evidenced by the steps taken over a century ago toward the formation of an international meteorological body. In 1853 representatives from a number of maritime countries met in Brussels [not in the form of a congress open to the public] in an effort to obtain collaboration on an international program for meteorological observations by ships at sea. For the next quarter century this sort of development went steadily ahead with meetings on various other meteorological subjects at such cities as Leipzig, Vienna, Utrecht, and London. Then in 1878, when there were enough national meteorological services to warrant the move, the International Meteorological Organization (IMO) was formed at a meeting at Utrecht in The Netherlands. To effect collaboration in disseminating weather information vital to the needs of the weather forecaster in an age of air travel, the IMO [has since its formation] through its Conference of Directors built up a system of regional commissions, technical commissions, and special working groups. Although not an intergovernmental body, the IMO achieved a remarkable cooperation between national meteorological services during the 70 years of its existence. Nevertheless, because of the ever-increasing importance of a global meteorology to many human activities, including civil aviation and merchant shipping, the need for a more official sponsorship became apparent. A World Meteorological Convention was therefore drawn up and adopted by the Conference of Directors of the IMO. The Convention provided for the transformation of the IMO into a new World Meteorological Organization (WMO).

The World Meteorological Organization, which is a specialized agency of the United Nations, held its first congress in Paris on March 19, 1951. Since that time its membership has grown from 44 to 116 sovereign states and territories. Included among the purposes of the WMO are cooperation in the establishment and maintenance of observing stations, the promotion of the rapid exchange of weather information, and the promotion of standardization of meteorological observation and publication.*

ᗰ History of Weather Forecasting

By the time the first international congress opened in 1873, the device most useful to meteorological research already had been invented. That invention was not, strictly speaking, a meteorological instrument. It was not a new barometer, nor a new type of rain gauge, nor a wind-velocity recorder: it was the electric telegraph. Because weather is an ever-changing process, the meteorologist is fairly helpless if he cannot find out—and the faster the better—what the weather is like elsewhere.

* From *Meteorological Satellites;* Staff Report prepared for the use of the Committee on Astronautical and Space Sciences, United States Senate, by the Library of Congress (87th Congress, 2d Session), March 29, 1962, p. 104.

It is for this reason that the earlier attempts, scientifically valiant as they were, are now merely historical notes. It is interesting to know, of course, that Ferdinand II, Duke of Tuscany (1610–1670), ordered the establishment of meteorological stations, actually just record-keeping establishments, in northern Italy as early as 1653. We now know that the area over which observations were made was much too small to be useful; even a meteorologist armed with today's theory of weather phenomena could not have done much good because the information would invariably have reached him too late, since the fastest way of getting it to him would have been on horseback.

There were other early keepers of weather records: Chief Justice Paul Bradley (of Massachusetts), who kept a meteorological diary of his area for the years from 1738–1750; the astronomer and physicist Professor John Winthrop (1714–1779) of Harvard who kept records from 1742–1778; and the Meteorological Society of the Palatinate (in southwest Germany), which operated over a fairly large area from 1780 to 1792. The Meteorological Society of the Palatinate published its records in detail until activities were terminated by the French Revolution. But one wonders how many of the readers of these publications must have come to the conclusion that their hands were tied for lack of a fast means of communication.

The first meteorologist to receive weather information by wire was the physicist Professor Joseph Henry (1797–1878) of the Smithsonian Institution in 1849. During the same year, G. J. Symons in England began to collect telegraphic weather reports from stations in his country, but an additional waiting period had to elapse because it took time to build telegraph lines. Only five years later in the United States there were weather observers of the Smithsonian Institution in 31 states, and by 1854 the number of stations had increased to 500. Then came the Civil War, which curtailed the Smithsonian Institution as effectively as the French Revolution had curtailed the Meteorological Society of the Palatinate.

It had become evident by then that weather reporting and forecasting had to be a public service, but now the legal problem arose as to how the legislature could establish such a service and how it should be organized.

On February 2, 1870, the House of Representatives passed a joint resolution authorizing the Secretary of War to provide [money and manpower needed] for the taking of meteorological observations in the interior of the continent, and for giving notice on the northern lakes and Atlantic seaboard of the approach and force of storms. The Senate concurred 3 days later and President Ulysses S. Grant [1822–1885] signed the measure on February 9.

On February 28, 1870, Secretary of War William W. Belknap [1829–1880] notified Colonel Albert J. Myer [1829–1880], Chief of the Signal Service, that the responsibility for the weather service would belong to the Signal Service (later to become the Signal Corps). Historically, it can be admitted that the only real asset possessed by the Signal Service for assuming the task was the possession of the necessary telegraphic facilities. Regular stations increased from 24 in 1870 to 55 in the following year. By June 1890, there was a total of 178 stations, but many of these were equipped to record only temperature and precipitation.

Despite the fact that this early meteorological service set an enviable record for public service in the years of its existence, it did not escape criticism, especially from the Congress. There remained always the belief of many that the national weather service properly belonged under civilian control. In 1887 the drive for civilian control gained strong support from a contemporary battle on the part of the agricultural interests for the creation of a Department of Agriculture. However, the final transfer of the weather service to the new Department of Agriculture was not achieved until July 1, 1891, when the U.S. Weather Bureau came into existence.

Whereas the public service rendered by the new Weather Bureau was rapidly expanded into new areas of public interest, the number of manned weather stations did not show a corresponding increase. For example (see Table 5), in 1893 there were 161 regular weather stations, but 30 years later this number had increased to only 200.*

Table 5

TOTAL NUMBER OF REGULAR WEATHER BUREAU STATIONS AT SELECTED INTERVALS

Year	Stations	Year	Stations	Year	Stations
1870	25	1907	195	1947	412
1871	60	1915	197	1950	394
1886	132	1923	200	1954	332
1893	161	1930	210	1955	314
1896	146	1941	302	1958	314
1899	159	1942	296	1960	315
1900	173	1945	439		
1905	180	1946	399		

The weather services of other countries expanded in a corresponding manner during the same period, but for the years from 1870 to 1923 it was, everywhere, just a horizontal expansion. The weather stations covered a larger area virtually every year, but there were severe limitations. One was the fundamental fact that about ¾ of our planet was covered by oceans; not even all the land area was inhabited, and even large portions of these areas were not inhabited by scientifically inclined people. As late as 1950 the total area covered by weather sta-

* From *Meteorological Satellites, op. cit.,* pp. 23–24.

tions amounted to about 5 per cent of the total surface area of the earth.

The other serious limitation was the fact that every weather station was ground based. The French meteorologist Léon P. Teisserenc de Bort (1855–1913) had, in 1898, divided the atmosphere into two layers. The upper layer was of rather uniform temperature and seemed to be stratified; Teisserenc de Bort called it the "stratosphere." The layer near the ground was constantly being turned over by various forces, hence Teisserenc de Bort, using the corresponding Greek word *tropos*, called it the "troposphere," stating that its upper limit was at approximately 10 kilometers (about 6 miles); he also stated that all the meteorological phenomena took place in the troposphere only.* But meteorologists could not even penetrate the troposphere regularly. During the nineteenth century some brave researchers made high-altitude balloon flights, with great danger to their own lives, and acquired valuable data. But this, even disregarding the danger, could be only an occasional event because of the expense involved. For a while there was hope that mountain stations might help, but these did not prove satisfactory.

But Mark W. Harrington [1848–1926], Chief of the U.S. Weather Bureau in 1893, reported that mountain stations had proved inadequate for aerological (upper-air) work and went on further to state that knowledge of the upper air at the time was insignificant and purely theoretical.

The new Weather Bureau, however, was soon to recognize that the secret of adequate weather forecasting was to be found in the upper atmosphere. Under a new chief, Willis L. Moore, the Bureau initiated experiments to sound the upper atmosphere on a more or less regular basis. In

---

* See Table 6, pages 48–51, for the modern subdivision of our atmosphere.

Table 6

DESCRIPTION OF ATMOSPHERIC SHELLS [LAYERS] CONTAINED IN THE INTERNATIONAL UNION OF GEODESY AND GEOPHYSICS RECOMMENDED NOMENCLATURE

Name	*Description*
	Temperature
Troposphere	The region nearest the surface, having a more or less uniform decrease of temperature with altitude. The nominal rate of temperature decrease is 6.5°K/km [Kelvin per kilometer equivalent to 19.2°F per mile], but inversions are common. The troposphere, the domain of weather, is in convective equilibrium [equalization mainly by convection] with the sun-warmed surface of the earth. The tropopause, which occurs at altitudes between 6 and 18 kilometers [3.7 to 11 miles] (higher and colder over the equator), is the domain of high winds and highest cirrus clouds.
Stratosphere	The region next above the troposphere and having a nominally constant temperature. The stratosphere is thicker over the poles, thinner or even nonexistent over the equator. Maximum of atmospheric ozone found near stratopause. Rare nacreous clouds also found near stratopause. Stratopause is at about 25 kilometers [15.5 miles] in middle latitudes. Stratospheric temperatures are in the order of arctic winter temperatures.

Name	*Description*
Mesosphere	The region of the first temperature maximum. The mesosphere lies above the stratosphere and below the major temperature minimum, which is found near 80 kilometers [50 miles] altitude and constitutes the mesopause. A relatively warm region between two cold regions; the region of disappearance of most meteors. The mesopause is found at altitudes of from 70 to 85 kilometers [43–53 miles]. Mesosphere is in radiative equilibrium between ultraviolet ozone heating by the upper fringe of ozone region and the infrared ozone and carbon-dioxide cooling by radiation to space.
Thermosphere	The region of rising temperature above the major temperature minimum at around 80 kilometers [50 miles] altitude. No upper-altitude limit. The domain of the aurorae. Temperature rise at base of thermosphere attributed to too infrequent collisions among molecules to maintain thermodynamic equilibrium. The potentially enormous infrared radiative cooling by carbon dioxide is not actually realized, owing to inadequate collisions.

COMPOSITION

Homosphere	The region of substantially uniform composition, in the sense of constant mean molecular weight, from the surface upward. The homopause is found at altitudes between

Table 6 (Continued)

Name	*Description*
	80 and 100 kilometers [50–62 miles]. The composition changes here primarily because of dissociation of oxygen. Mean molecular weight decreases accordingly. The ozonosphere, having its peak concentration near stratopause altitude, does not change the mean molecular weight of the atmosphere significantly.
Heterosphere	The region of significantly varying composition above the homosphere and extending indefinitely outward. The "molecular weight" of air diminishes from 29 to about 90 kilometers [56 miles] to 16 at about 500 kilometers [311 miles]. Well above the level of oxygen dissociation, nitrogen begins to dissociate and diffusive separation (lighter atoms and molecules rising to the top) sets in.

IONIZATION

| Ionosphere | The region of sufficiently large electron density to affect radio communication. However, only about 1 molecule in 1,000 in the F_2 region * to 1 in 100,000,000 in the D |

---

* There are 4 ionized regions in the upper atmosphere, the D layer at between 45 and 50 miles, the E layer at 70 to 80 miles, the F_1 layer at 150 miles, and the F_2 layer at about 300 miles. The old designation of Kennelly–Heaviside layer later became known as D and E. Each layer reflects radio waves of a different wavelength; only the very short waves, such as are used in television, pass through all of them. This is the reason why long-distance television broadcasts are impossible without satellites.

Name	*Description*
	region is ionized. The bottom of the ionosphere, the D region, is found at about 80 kilometers [50 miles] during the day. At night the D region disappears and the bottom of the ionosphere rises to 100 kilometers [62 miles]. The top of the ionosphere is not well defined but has often been taken as about 400 kilometers [248 miles]. The recent extension upward to 1,000 kilometers [621 miles] based on satellite and rocket data is shown.

CHEMICAL REACTIONS

Chemosphere	The region where chemical activity (primarily photochemical) is predominant. The chemosphere is found within the altitude limits of about 20 to 110 kilometers [12–70 miles].

MOLECULAR ESCAPE

Exosphere	The region wherein molecular escape from the earth's atmosphere is significant. The base of the exosphere, the critical level, is thought to be at an altitude above 300 kilometers [186 miles], possibly as high as 1,000 kilometers [621 miles]. Satellite data indicating higher densities at these altitudes favor higher exosphere levels. Lighter atoms and molecules can escape at lower altitudes than heavier ones. The earth's magnetic field effectively prevents the escape of charged particles, however.[1]

the summer of 1895, experiments were begun with instrumented kites, and some success was achieved. The primary limitations to the system, however, were the facts that soundings could be obtained only under fair-weather conditions and with surface winds in access of 10 to 15 miles per hour. Furthermore, the kite was limited to relatively low-level soundings, around 7,000 to 8,000 feet, although records in excess of 23,000 feet were established. Sixteen kite stations were in operation in 1898, but activities were limited to the months between April and November. Nevertheless, the kite network existed for over 30 years or until the kite observations were superseded by observations from aircraft. The last kite station, at Ellendale, Nebraska, was closed in 1933. Captive balloons carrying meteorological instruments were also experimented with during this period, but they proved to be less efficient than kites in achieving useful altitudes.

Through the use of free [sounding] balloons, extreme altitudes greater than 90,000 feet were achieved as early as 1910, but since the recordings could be evaluated only upon descent and recovery of the instruments attached, such observations proved useful only for climatological and research purposes. The time delay between launch and recovery was usually a matter of days and often of weeks, which, of course, rendered the soundings [findings] useless for the preparation of the upper-air synoptic charts needed on a current basis by the weather forecaster.

The real impetus for upper-air observation, however, was the rise of civil and military aviation in the early 1920s. The increasing demand for aviation forecasts fol-

Water-vapor spectroscope at a mountain station in 1939, Table Mountain, California.

Until the early 1930s kites like this box kite were used to carry weather-recording instruments aloft.

Early equipment, such as this balloon carrying a 4-candle lantern, was sent aloft for upper-wind observations at night.

lowing World War I brought an expansion of upper-wind observing stations. From the beginning, Weather Bureau pilot-balloon observations were highly successful, and greater altitudes were achieved by American equipment and procedures than were being accomplished in European countries that were establishing upper-air networks. By the middle thirties, the heights of daytime [good-weather] flights were averaging 30,000 to 45,000 feet with nighttime averages above 10,000 feet. In 1930, 45 Weather Bureau stations provided upper-air wind data by means of pilot balloons. By 1932 this number doubled and remained fairly constant thereafter until World War II. The majority of these stations maintained a schedule of 4 soundings per day. A rapid expansion of pilot-balloon stations immediately preceded the attack on Pearl Harbor in 1941 by the establishment of over 50 new stations.

Nevertheless, wind observations by pilot balloons did not supply the detailed information on temperatures, humidities, and pressures aloft that was required by the weather forecaster. Prior to the discontinuance of the cumbersome kite program previously described, meteorologists had experimented with aircraft-borne sensing equipment. Experiments were successfully conducted at San Diego in 1925 by the Weather Bureau, and the Weather Bureau and the Navy cooperated the same year in a similar program at the Anacostia Naval Air Station in the District of Columbia. But it was not until July 1, 1931, that the aviation interests finally persuaded the Weather Bureau to undertake daily airplane observations (known as Apobs) at Chicago, Cleveland, Dallas, and Omaha. Altitudes of 14,000 to

An observation plane with electric recording equipment mounted in wing struts, 1935.

Recording equipment, electro-meteorograph, used in U.S. Weather Bureau airplanes.

17,000 were normal. By 1938 daily flights were made from 30 locations, 17 of them operated by the military services. However, all Apob stations were discontinued before the outbreak of World War II with the introduction of the far superior *radiosonde* [a balloon-carried instrument package transmitting information on temperature, pressure, and humidity by radio. See opposite page]. The most successful of these instruments had been developed in Russia prior to the mid-1930s, but by 1935 U.S. scientists had developed a successful instrument. The radiosonde, even in the early

Electrometeorograph mounted between wings of weather observation airplane.

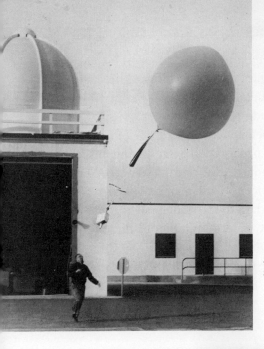

A radiosonde being sent aloft.

Radiosonde carrying pressure, temperature, and humidity indicators. Sonde transmits information to ground stations by radio.

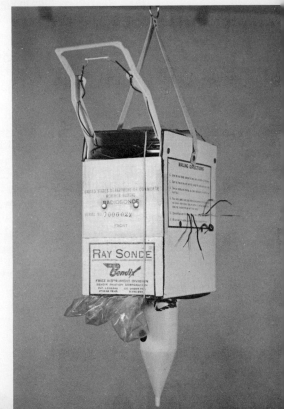

experiments, obtained altitudes in excess of 50,000 feet and usually without regard to the weather. The observations also proved to be cheaper than those obtained by aircraft. In 1938, 6 radiosonde stations were established; by 1941 this number had been increased to 34. Similar developments in upper-air observation were taking place also in other countries; and by the end of World War II, the meteorological services of all major countries were contributing upper-air data to the daily pool of those available to the meteorologist. A large fraction of these foreign stations had been established originally during the war by one or the other of the two U.S. military weather services.*

ꊍ Rockets as Aids in Weather Research

World War II also had brought a fundamental innovation, namely, the large German V-2 rockets. These rockets, of which, as mentioned earlier, the United States assembled about 75 from captured parts, could carry a full ton of scientific instruments to an altitude of about 100 miles. This, of course, meant fantastic progress for upper-air research, but it had drawbacks somewhat similar to the manned flights of one century earlier. V-2 shots were expensive, they needed a trained firing crew, and there was some danger involved—this time to people on the ground who might be struck by the falling rocket. Hence, such shots could be made only where the danger factor could be eliminated, on designated proving grounds or at sea.

For purposes of meteorological research smaller rockets like the liquid-fuel using Aerobee were developed (the Aerobee

* From *Meteorological Satellites, op. cit.,* pp. 25–26.

by Aerojet–General and Douglas Aircraft). These carried a smaller load than the V-2, but there was no need for a 1-ton payload each time. However, they went to about the same altitude as the V-2 and were much cheaper and easier to handle because of their small size. Another way of using rockets for meteorological research was developed by the great American scientist Dr. James A. Van Allen, then Professor of Physics at Iowa University. A small, solid-fuel rocket, fired from the ground, could reach an altitude of about 60,000 feet. But if the same rocket were lifted by a balloon to 60,000 feet where all the dense and resistant layers of the atmosphere have been left below, the rocket could reach an altitude of around 50 miles. This balloon-launched rocket became known as the *rockoon*.

One version of such a rockoon is described in the Annals of the International Geophysical Year (IGY) as follows: [2]

Loki-Phase II rockoon. The rockoon is the general term for a balloon-launched rocket. The rocket used in this work is a modified Loki-Phase II [a solid-fuel rocket developed by the U.S. Army], known as the Hawk. The propulsion unit itself is a solid-fuel unit 3 inches in diameter and 4 feet long. In its nose it carries a typical 8.5 pound payload of scientific instruments. The nose is also 3 inches in diameter and about 36 inches in length.

The rockoon is launched from shipboard. A 45-foot balloon is inflated on the ship and released, carrying the rocket suspended on a long nylon line. When the balloon reaches an altitude of about 75,000 feet, the rocket is automatically fired by a pressure switch and flies nearly vertically upward to an altitude of about 75 miles.

Over 50 of these rockoons are being fired during the IGY, in regions stretching from the Arctic to the Antarctic, to obtain information on cosmic-ray particles at high altitudes and on ultraviolet and X rays emitted by the sun during periods of solar flares.

The weight lifted by the balloon is as follows:

	Pounds
Complete rocket, including payload	32.0
Firing box	3.5
Radiosonde	2.0
Load line and fittings	3.0

This technique was developed at the State University of Iowa, and has been successfully used from shipboard in the Arctic during the summers of 1952, 1953, 1954, and 1955. The Naval Research Laboratory also used this technique in the Arctic in 1954 and 1955, and off the coast of California in September 1956. By means of the balloon launch it is possible to escape the air drag of the dense lower atmosphere and thus to achieve quite high altitudes with a small inexpensive rocket. New miniaturized electronic circuits make it possible to pack a full scientific experiment, complete with radio transmitter and necessary batteries, within a total payload weight of 8 pounds.

The advantages of the rockoon techniques are:

1. The vehicular cost is markedly less than that of any other available system for delivering small payloads (6 to 40 pounds) to altitudes of the order of 100 kilometers [62 miles].

2. Owing to the small size and light weight of rockets typically launched from balloons (gross launching weight, 30 to 210 pounds), the field handling of rockoons requires a party of only about four men and almost no special facilities.

3. Since the firing of the rocket occurs at altitudes where

the air density is only a few per cent of that at sea level, the problem of aerodynamic heating is greatly reduced.

The consequences of advantages (1) and (2) are quite far reaching in certain types of investigations. In typical cases 10 rockoon firings have been made for the same total expenditure of funds for equipment and personnel as would have been required for a single firing of a large rocket launched from sea level. The first, and thus far only, high-altitude measurements in the Arctic have been made by the rockoon technique. The first rocket measurements that have a comprehensive coverage in geographical position have been made with rockoons. . . . It is likely that rockoon flights can be successfully conducted with relatively infrequent weather delays from various islands in the Pacific, in the Caribbean, etc. The use of clusters of small rubber balloons [instead of a single larger plastic balloon] will further reduce the limitations of surface winds.*

ꛃ The Weather Ships

Though the distinction is sometimes uncertain, the field of meteorology is divided into two main areas. One is that of weather research, striving to find facts and factors on which a theory can be built, then to be tested by additional experiments, such as rockoon flights. The other area is that which uses existing theory and the most recent observations for the purpose of making forecasts. There, the problem is not only necessary speed, which has been achieved in the age of teletype, teleprinters, and telephone, but also the volume of information. Even if the reports available are numerous, they may not cover the area about which the forecaster must know at that moment.

* From *Meteorological Satellites, op. cit.,* p. 21.

On one occasion before 1950, in the early days of the White Sands Proving Ground, while an important rocket shot was in preparation, the weather was inappropriate, to use a mild term. The weather forecaster was nearly helpless; the cloud-covered area extended almost unbroken between White Sands in New Mexico and the Los Angeles area, which was the westernmost report obtainable. To make a forecast the meteorologist had to know how far to the west the cloud cover extended over the ocean, but at that time he could not find this information.

This forecaster's predicament is echoed in the following extract, which gives interesting statistics about the extent of meteorological work.

The working laboratory of meteorology is the entire world atmosphere, and its size and inaccessibility account in large part for the slow development of meteorology. It has been physically impossible for the weather scientist to observationally sample the tremendous volume of the atmosphere with sufficient completeness to fully comprehend its vagaries, let alone make always accurate forecasts.

It is estimated that there are today more than 100,000 surface weather-observing stations throughout the world. The bulk of these, however, do not regularly report to meteorological forecast or operational centers but are maintained primarily for climatological purposes. Many of these stations record only maximum and minimum temperatures and/or precipitation amounts; others may maintain a more sophisticated record but limit their support to research or special local uses. Nevertheless, there remains an enormous, although unevenly distributed, network composed of something like 8,500 observing stations that regularly report to synoptic collection centers from 4 to 24 (or more) times daily. Each "observation" covers a number of factors such as temperature, humidity, atmospheric pressures, wind speed and direction, precipitation, visibility, and cloudiness. Each set of such data is transmitted by teletype or radio in a universally understood code, to be received and retransmitted from central, longer-range transmitting stations to hundreds of forecasting centers distributed over most of the globe.

Most of the weather observations that cover the world oceans are obtained from the 3,500 or so ships belonging to the World Meteorological Organization's "selected ship scheme." This is a scheme whereby certain carefully selected merchant ships sailing under a variety of flags voluntarily make various weather observations, which are transmitted by them to form part of the worldwide meteorological network of today. What is perhaps most interesting is that these ships are providing information that may well be in many ways more useful to aircraft and to weather forecasters than to the ships themselves. For over the land, aircraft and the weather forecaster can rely on several thousand stations, making observations several times a day. But over vast areas of the seas, they may have nothing but this voluntary service to give them an idea of weather conditions. . . .

The stationary weather ships established since World War II through international effort give some stability to the reporting network and serve in addition as platforms for upper atmospheric soundings and other more sophisticated (and probably more accurate) types of observations along the important transoceanic air lanes and in other areas of critical interest to the meteorologist. At the present time, 9 weather ships are in operation in the North Atlantic and are maintained individually by the United States, Canada, the United Kingdom, and the Scandinavian countries. West Germany contributes financially to the over-all Atlantic ship program but does not itself maintain a weather vessel.*

However, all this, as has been said earlier, does not add up to a significant percentage of the earth's surface. Even with all the electronic-communication means available, it takes time to put the information together. In fact, it might take more time than there is, since the weather situation can undergo considerable changes while the map is being made.

⊠   TV in the Sky

The ultimate wish of the meteorologist has been for an over-all view of the weather over a very large area, at least as large as a continent, so that the main trends could be perceived literally at a glance. In 1930 this would have been called a meteorologist's dream. But by 1950 the theoretical means of realizing this dream was in sight: a television camera in orbit around the earth.

The first formal proposal to utilize a satellite vehicle was advanced by S. M. Greenfield and W. W. Kellogg of Kellogg Laboratories, Inc. in a classified USAF Project Rand report dated April 1951. The report remained classified until August 1960 when an unclassified edition was published by the Rand Corporation.[3]

The purpose of the Rand investigation is summarized in the first paragraph of its introductory summary:

The value of observing the weather over inaccessible areas by aerial weather reconnaissance has been recog-

* From *Meteorological Satellites, op. cit.,* p. 9.

Composite of films taken by a camera in an Atlas missile during a 5,000-mile flight with maximum altitude of 700 miles.

nized for many years. An alternative method of obtaining broad coverage of the weather, however, is thought to lie in the use of a special satellite vehicle that could observe cloud patterns. It is obvious that any meteorological recoinnaissance utilizing only observations from such a high-altitude "eye" cannot provide quantitative values for the parameters normally associated with standard weather observation and forecasting techniques. In determining the feasibility of such a system, therefore, the questions that must be answered are: (1) What extent of coverage can be expected from a satellite viewing system? (2) In terms of resolution and contrast, what can be seen from the satellite? (3) Given proper coverage and resolution, what can actually be determined regarding the synoptic weather situation from this information?

The report, which concerned itself solely with an analysis based primarily on cloud observations, presented

This photograph taken at an altitude of 250 miles shows (lower left) Puerto Rico, and (right) Haiti and the Dominican Republic.

several systematic methods for converting such data into information of value to the weather forecaster. Their suggested methods of attack on the problem of analysis and utilization of the satellite cloud pictures consisted of the following:

1. It is suggested that a typing of clouds as to *cause* rather than *appearance* will greatly facilitate the identification of the synoptic situation. Classification into two main categories would constitute a possible breakdown, as follows: (*a*) Regional clouds (those caused by purely local conditions), and (*b*) migrating cloud systems (clouds that appear to move as a unit). This breakdown

might then be coupled with a knowledge of the clouds associated with various weather phenomena to complete the synoptic picture.

2. It is a recognized fact that similar synoptic situations occurring under different climatic and/or topographic conditions may produce radically different weather. A statistical analysis is therefore suggested, in which (a) the desired area is divided into small regions of similar climate, geography, etc., and (b) a statistical survey of cloud types and associated weather found with various weather situations (fronts, etc.) in each region is made.

3. Owing to the fact that identification of fronts as fronts may be very difficult, it is suggested that it may

The white area at the left shows a weather front over the Atlantic photographed at an altitude of 750 miles.

be possible to identify air masses from high-altitude pictures and to utilize them in the formulation of the synoptic picture. Since general classifications of air masses include as integral identifying features the stability of the air, the moisture, and the type of clouds produced in a given air mass, this should not be too difficult, in many cases. An air mass identification has the further advantage of establishing more closely the possible limits of the various meteorological parameters.

4. A major advantage of satellite weather observations is the repeated broad spatial coverage. Such broad coverage provides the meteorologist with an essential element for his analysis, which is generally referred to as *continuity*. It permits him to follow a given system as it moves and develops over a period of days. It is a relatively simple matter to identify a system once it is known that such a system is present. Once a weather situation is so identified, it can be earmarked from high-altitude pictures, and not only may it then be tracked across an inaccessible area like an ocean, but any over-all changes or modifications that affect the visible parameters may be almost immediately noticed. It is also likely that, having a complete analysis of the surrounding territory on land, where observations are plentiful, and many satellite observations of the unknown area (through which it is possible to get fixes on systems and to examine visually the over-all weather picture), a complete analysis of the desired region will become a much simpler thing to construct.

Each of the above suggestions affords excellent possibilities of providing the required information. It should be kept in mind, however, that these suggestions appear

(*Opposite*) An early attempt at orbiting a satellite for cloud-cover observation, Vanguard II, in summer, 1958.

Tiros I under cover before firing in April 1960. Its 2 television cameras transmitted 22,596 photographs of weather phenomena.

to offer the best solution when systematically used together.*

This report was essentially a feasibility study, which accounts, in part, for its very cautious language. The concept of a weather satellite was helped along very considerably by a lucky rocket shot; the photographs from V-2 No. 20 fired from the White Sands Proving Ground. The date was March 7, 1947, the altitude about 100 miles. As T. A. Bergstralh wrote:

* From *Meteorological Satellites, op. cit.*, pp. 26–27.

98

A Tiros rocket being given a vibration test at the Astro-
Electronic Products Division of RCA, Princeton, New Jersey.

Picture of Hokkaido, the northernmost Japanese island, transmitted by Tiros I in its eighth orbit and received at the Kaena Point, Hawaii station.

On March 7, 1947, the twentieth V-2 to be launched in America took to the air from the Army Ordnance Proving Ground at White Sands, New Mexico. As on several of the previous flights, an attempt was made to obtain photographs of the features of interest on the rocket, and, of course, of the earth. In this attempt the effort met with considerable success. Included among the group of pictures obtained are the first ever to be taken from altitudes greater than 160 kilometers (100 miles). The quality of the photographs is fairly good. For the first time, in pictures taken at such high altitudes, it is possible to recognize clearly many geographical features. In addition a large number and variety of cloud formations were re-

corded by the cameras and other information of meteorological value.

The appearance of the earth is unquestionably the most
striking feature of the photographs. The Colorado River,

Sketch of the operation system in Tiros II designed to collect data on radiation reflected or emitted by the earth and
its atmosphere.

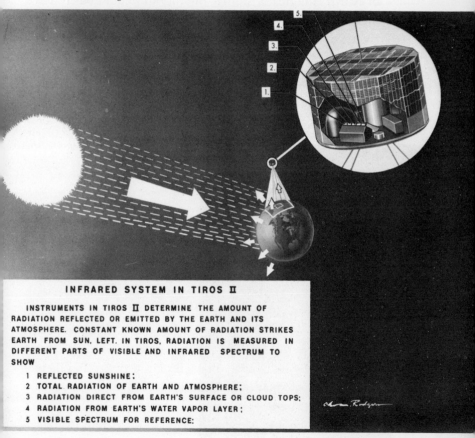

INFRARED SYSTEM IN TIROS II

INSTRUMENTS IN TIROS II DETERMINE THE AMOUNT OF
RADIATION REFLECTED OR EMITTED BY THE EARTH AND ITS
ATMOSPHERE. CONSTANT KNOWN AMOUNT OF RADIATION STRIKES
EARTH FROM SUN, LEFT. IN TIROS, RADIATION IS MEASURED IN
DIFFERENT PARTS OF VISIBLE AND INFRARED SPECTRUM TO
SHOW

1 REFLECTED SUNSHINE;
2 TOTAL RADIATION OF EARTH AND ATMOSPHERE;
3 RADIATION DIRECT FROM EARTH'S SURFACE OR CLOUD TOPS;
4 RADIATION FROM EARTH'S WATER VAPOR LAYER;
5 VISIBLE SPECTRUM FOR REFERENCE;

the Gulf of California, the peninsula of Lower California, and the Pacific Ocean beyond are all clearly discernible in [a picture] which was taken as the rocket reached the peak of its trajectory. More than 200,000 square miles of the United States and Mexico are visible between the bottom of the picture below the rocket and the curved horizon 900 miles to the west. If the V-2 had risen in another part of North America, a similar photograph could easily have included both New York and Chicago. Many lesser lakes, rivers, dry lakes, etc., have been identified.*

* From *Naval Research Laboratory Report* No. R–3082, 1947. Reprinted in *Meteorological Satellites, op. cit.,* p. 28.

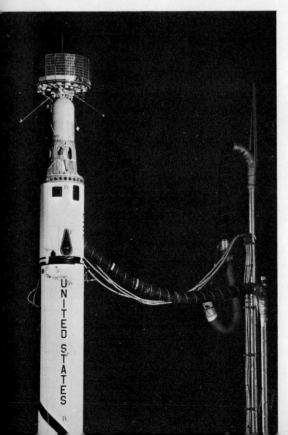

Tiros II payload mounted on a Thor-Delta rocket at its launching site.

Tiros III being given a spin test at RCA's Astro-Electronic Division.

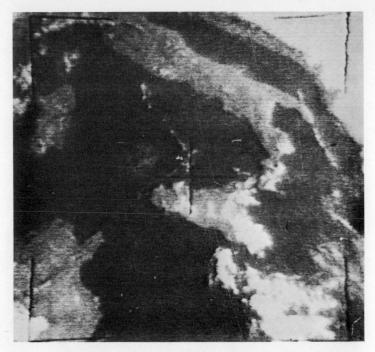

Tiros III's picture of the Mediterranean area, made during
its 878th orbit, September 11, 1961. Italy, Sicily, Sardinia,
and Tunisia are visible.

Early in May, 1954, Dr. Harry Wexler of the U.S. Weather
Bureau publicly stated, on the occasion of the Third Symposium
on Space Travel at the Hayden Planetarium in New York City,
the desirability of a weather satellite. After several other scientists had gone on record as favoring weather satellites, another lucky rocket shot occurred, described by Otto Berg of the
Naval Research Laboratory and L. F. Hubert of the U.S.
Weather Bureau, as follows:

For almost a decade the Naval Research Laboratory of
Washington, D.C., has been engaged actively in the field of

high-altitude photography from rockets. The principal purpose has been to obtain pictures of the earth so that the rocket aspect (its orientation in space during flight) could be determined. To obtain this aspect information it is desirable that recognizable features of the earth's surface be photographed, an objective best attained when there is a minimum of cloud cover. For that reason and because optical tracking from the ground is also desirable, rockets

Hurricane "Betsy" the 200-mile white "eye" at left, photographed by Tiros III on September 7, 1961.

are seldom fired if the cloudiness exceeds 10 per cent. Consequently, photographs from rockets have not provided much information relative to large areas of clouds.

A fortunate exception occurred on October 5, 1954. Two rocketborne movie cameras obtained pictures of towering clouds spiraling into a tropical storm near Del Rio, Texas. The pictures may well launch the era of rocket photoreconnaissance for meteorology. In the near future more rocket pictures of hurricanes will be made, for plans are

A photograph of Hurricane "Esther" about 900 miles east of Cuba transmitted by Tiros III on September 16, 1961.

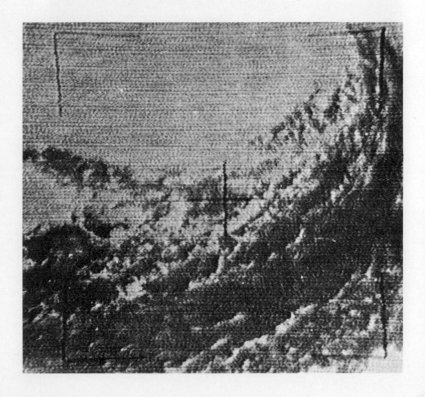

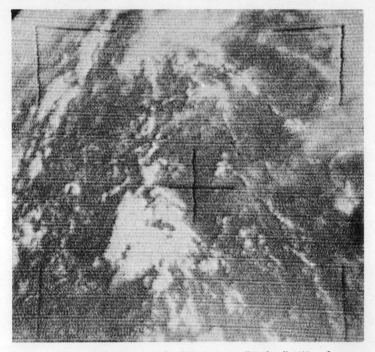

Tiros III's photograph of Hurricane "Esther" 150 miles east of Norfolk, Virginia, September 19, 1961.

already going ahead to fire rockets for that specific purpose. Techniques that will be developed by rocket reconnaissance of hurricanes may find wider application in an expanded program of ultra-high altitude meteorological reconnaissance. . . .

The possibilities suggested by this accidental rocket reconnaissance of a tropical storm are tremendous. One obvious use is already being planned—rocket photography of hurricanes. There are many unsolved problems in meteorology that may be vulnerable to this approach, however.

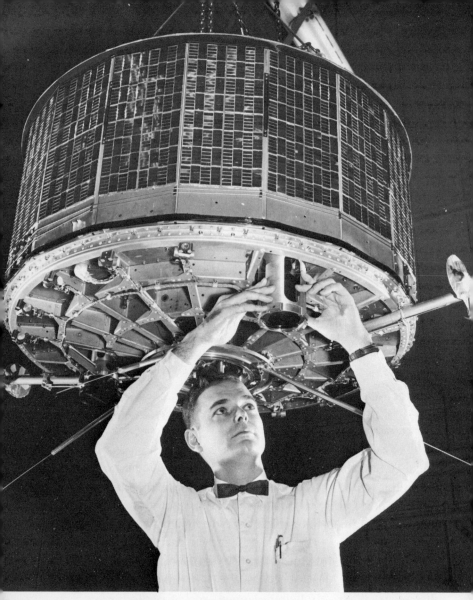

The medium-angle Tegea lens, being installed in Tiros IV at RCA's Astro-Electronic Division, made clearer photographs from satellites possible.

Vast regions of the earth are still meteorologically unexplored territory. For example, the important meteorological zone across equatorial Africa and South America has been described in only the crudest detail. The fact that huge amounts of rain are precipitated along this zone makes it quite important to several problems. Rocket photography has the advantage of providing truly simultaneous data, albeit of a specialized nature. Rocket and aircraft reconnaissance, then, may well supplement each other in a highly successful manner.*

By 1955 there was no longer any doubt that photographs from positions at the fringe of and beyond the atmosphere would give meteorologists what they had been dreaming about: over-all views of very large areas with clearly discernible cloud formations. Plans were made for incorporating a meteorological satellite in the program for the International Geophysical Year beginning in 1957. But the ideal case, the television camera in orbit, could not yet be realized. The satellite program was to be carried out completely by the Vanguard rocket, which did not have the necessary carrying capacity. All that Vanguard could carry was a few photocells sensitive to infrared (heat) rays; these would give an indication how much of the sun's radiation received by the earth is reradiated into space by: (*a*) land not covered by clouds; (*b*) ocean not covered by clouds; (*c*) cloud cover, either over land or over sea; and (*d*) the polar regions. But the third Vanguard rocket that was to carry this device failed to orbit. The fourth Vanguard, which did put the satellite called Vanguard II into orbit in 1958, carried 2 photocells sensitive to visible light. The cells worked, but the satellite wobbled so much that it was virtually impossible to interpret the pictures.

The first satellite to produce a cloud-cover picture was Explorer VI, launched in 1959. For useful results, however, the

* *Ibid.*, pp. 30–31.

meteorological researchers and everybody else had to wait for a satellite especially built for this purpose.

This was Tiros I (see pages 70–72), lifted into orbit on April 1, 1960 by a Thor-Able 3-stage rocket (Able refers to an extra upper stage of the Thor missile). The drum-shaped Tiros I was 42 inches in diameter with a height of 19 inches and weighed 270 pounds.

It was equipped with 2 television cameras, which were identical, except for their lens systems. One was a low-resolution camera with an f 1.5 lens; the other was a high resolution camera with an f 1.8 lens. Each camera had its own tape recorder with a capacity of 32 photographs, taken at 30-second intervals. Power for the equipment and the broadcasting was supplied by nickel-cadmium batteries constantly recharged by 9,200 solar cells.

Tiros I showed not only that the weather-reporting satellite could be made to work; its success was superior to what anyone would have dared to prophesy.

Tiros II (see pages 73, 74) followed on November 23, 1960. It weighed 10 pounds more than the first. In addition to the equipment of the first Tiros, there were radiation-sensing devices to report on the temperature of the cloud layers (their upper surfaces) and of the ground.

Tiros III (see pages 103–107), IV (see pages 108, 111, 113), and V (see page 112) followed at about half-year intervals as replacements of the earlier satellites (in some, 1 of the cameras failed to function properly after a while). They were equipped with additional radiation-measurement devices. But this series of Tiros shots was not yet the weather-satellite system that had been envisaged; it was the forerunner of such a system, designed to find out just what a weather satellite had to carry.

The first series of weather satellites to be tied into a ground system will be Project Nimbus (see page 113), to be ready in 1964, which will be in a different orbit—one almost over the poles. That way the entire globe will be covered twice a day.

And after Nimbus the final weather satellite is going to be Project Aeros, proposed for 1965, which will be in a rather distant orbit, 22,300 miles above sea level, over the equator. The reason for this distant orbit is that it has a special property. The Echo satellite, orbiting the earth about 1,000 miles out, needs just about 2 hours to complete an orbit. A satellite in a nearly circular orbit 4,000 miles out would need 4 hours for 1 orbit. A satellite 7,700 miles out would need 7 hours. At the distance of 22,300 miles, the orbital period becomes 24 hours. If such a satellite orbits the earth over the equator, it will seem to stand still over one spot, since the earth also needs 24 hours to turn on its axis once. Hence, such satellites are called *stationary* or *synchronous* satellites.

A few years ago the 24-hour orbit was considered as too far away to produce usable pictures. But in the meantime the television camera systems have been improved enough to make the use of this orbit possible. With 4 such satellites in the 24-hour orbit, the daytime coverage of the earth will be virtually continuous, extending over the whole cloud cover—or lack of it—

Final equipment tests on Tiros IV at RCA's Astro-Electronic Division.

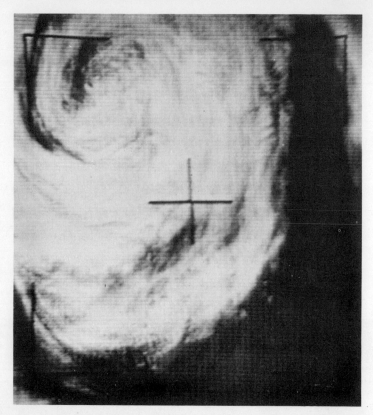

A storm off the northeast coast of Newfoundland photographed by Tiros V.

from 50° northern latitude to 50° southern latitude. An additional 13° at either end will be covered partially.

Then, with constant and up-to-the-hour information about cloud-cover and air-mass movements over most of the earth, weather forecasting will reach a state of perfection undreamed of in 1930. The general weather situation will be known for a long time in advance. And, though advance knowledge cannot prevent natural catastrophes, they will at least, be expected and

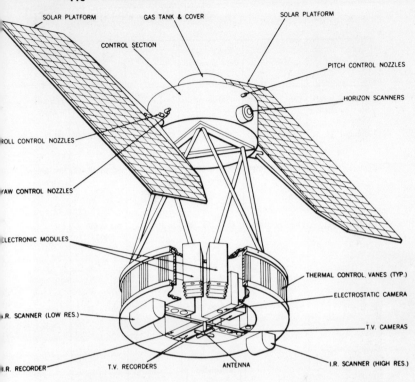

Outline drawing of a Nimbus weather satellite.

One of the first of Tiros IV's pictures. Visible at the bottom left are Lake Michigan and a strip of Lake Superior.

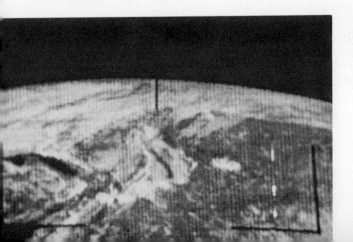

Table 7

SATELLITES CARRYING EQUIPMENT

Satellite	Launch date	Date when data reception ended	Orbit inclination	Altitude in miles	Coverage of globe
Vanguard satellite launching vehicle 3.	Sept. 26, 1958.	Did not orbit.	Did not orbit.	Did not orbit.	Did not orbit.
Vanguard II.....	Feb. 17, 1959..	Mar. 7, 1959.	32.88°	347 to 2,064.	33° N. to 33° S.
Explorer VI......	Aug. 7, 1959..	Not available.	48°	156 to 26,357.	Not available.
Explorer VII....	Oct. 13, 1959..	Oct. 13, 1960.	50.3°	342 to 680 (800?).	50° N. to 50° S.
TIROS I	Apr. 1, 1960..	June 29, 1960*.	48.3°	430 to 468...	...do.....
TIROS II.......	Nov. 23, 1960..	{ Suspended remote wide-angle camera operation, Jan. 18, 1961. Final cutoff, Dec. 3, 1961. }	48.5°	387 to 453...	...do.....
TIROS III.......	July 12, 1961..	Operating	48°	460.75 to 506.52.	...do.....

Sensing equipment of meteorological interest	Area viewed and resolution	Types of observation	Remarks
2 infrared photocells.	....	Roughly map cloud cover.	Did not orbit.
2 photocells sensitive to visible light.	Area, 6 to 30 miles	Roughly map daytime cloud cover	Wobble made data too difficult to interpret.
Elementary scanning device.	Low resolution...	Took first sketchy TV-type pictures of earth.	1 picture assembled and released; little meteorological value.
6 radiation sensors (Suomi's experiment).	Not available.	Solar, reflected, and reradiated infrared radiation for thermal radiation balance.	Data for research.
Wide-angle-TV camera.	Area, 700 to 800 miles. Resolution, about 2 miles.	Daytime cloud cover..	Research; some operational use.
Narrow-angle TV camera.	Area, 70 to 80 miles. Resolution, about ½ mile.	Snow and ice cover	Research.
Same cameras as TIROS I.	Same as TIROS I	Same as TIROS I....	Research; some operational use. Wide-angle camera out of focus.
Radiation sensors	450 miles	Thermal radiation balance.	Research.
	30 miles	Temperature of earth surface and cloud tops. Temperature and water vapor variation in tropopause.	
2 wide-angle cameras.	About 2 miles...	Daytime cloud, snow, and ice cover.	Camera No. 1 inoperative.
Explorer VII-type radiation sensors. (Suomi.)	About 450 miles.	Thermal radiation balance.	
2 radiometers ...	30 and 300 miles.	Radiation in specific wavelength bands.	

Table 7

SATELLITES CARRYING EQUIPMENT

Satellite	Launch date	Date when data reception ended	Orbit inclination	Altitude in miles	Coverage of globe
TIROS IV (3 more planned).	Feb. 8, 1962...	Operating ...	48°	475 to 500...	...do.....
Early Nimbus...	Proposed for 1962–63.	....	80° (retrograde).	680 (600 nautical).	Entire globe twice a day.
Later Nimbus...	Proposed for 1964–70.	....	....	....	....
Aeros	Proposed for 1965.	....	"Stationary" over equator.	22,300	50° N. to 50° S.[1]

FOR METEOROLOGICAL OBSERVATIONS

Sensing equipment of meteorological interest	Area viewed and resolution	Types of observation	Remarks
Same as TIROS III except new lens on one wide-angle camera	New lens. Area, about 450 miles. Resolution, about 1.5 miles.	Same as TIROS III...	
Improved TV cameras.	Area from horizon to horizon. Resolution, about ½ mile.	Greater detail of daytime cloud, snow, and ice cover.	
	300 miles	Thermal radiation balance.	
Radiation sensors	30 miles	Temperature of earth's surface or cloud tops and others. Limited solar spectral measurements.	
	5 miles	Nighttime cloud cover.	
Radiation sensors	....	Partial temperature soundngs of cloudless upper troposphere and stratosphere to obtain temperature structure. Time variations in solar spectra. Vertical distribution of water vapor, ozone, carbon dioxide.	
Radar	....	Detection of precipitation areas; possibly height, type, and vertical structure of clouds.	
Sferics	....	Detection of thunderstorms.	
Stationary TV cameras.	Resolution, 1 to 3 miles.	Daytime cloud cover...	
Movable TV camera.	Resolution, ¼ to ¾ mile.	Specific weather system under surveillance.	With 4 satellites, nearly continuous daytime cloud cover.
Possibly infrared camera.	....	Nighttime cloud cover.	

[1] Partial coverage up to 63°. Nearly continuous global coverage with 4 Aeros satellites. (Between 50° N. and 50° S.)

predicted. Counter measures can then be prepared for at comparative leisure.

REFERENCES

1. From USAF *Handbook of Geophysics,* revised edition.

2. Berkner, L. V., *Rockets and Satellites. Annals,* International Geophysical Year, vol. 6, 1958, pp. 56–57, 88–89.

3. Greenfield, S. M., and Kellogg, W. W. Unclassified edition of USAF Project Rand Report R-218, *Inquiry into the Feasibility of Weather Reconnaissance from a Satellite Vehicle.* Rand Corporation, Report R-365, August 1960.

4 Communication Satellites

OF ALL the possible types of artificial satellites, it is the communication satellites that will have the most direct impact on everyday life, as the recently orbited satellite Telstar has demonstrated.

Interestingly enough, the first proposal for the utilization of artificial satellites also dealt with "comsats," as they are often called. This proposal was made in an article by Arthur C. Clarke, the well-known British writer of science fiction, in the October 1945 issue of the English magazine *Wireless World*. It was also the first article dealing with *unmanned* artificial satellites; the earlier German * proposals concerned manned satellites, the type now usually called *space stations*.

In his article entitled "Extraterrestrial Relays" Clarke first pointed out that ground-based radio and television stations are not quite satisfactory if worldwide communication is the goal. His article began:

Although it is possible, by a suitable choice of frequencies and routes, to provide telephony circuits between any

* Proposals made by Hermann Oberth in *Die Rakete zu den Planetenräumen* ("The Rocket into Interplanetary Space"), Munich, 1923, manned satellite at an unspecified distance; Hermann Noordung in *Das Problem der Befahrung des Weltraumes* ("The Problem of Travel in Space"), Munich, 1929, manned station consisting of 3 units in the 24-hour orbit; Guido von Pirquet in *Die Rakete,* 1928 and 1929, 3 manned stations in 3 different orbits, 1 of the 3 in an orbit touching the other 2 orbits, to be used as a shuttle between the 2 main stations.

119

two points or regions of the earth for a large part of the time, long-distance communciation is greatly hampered by the peculiarities of the ionosphere, and there are even occasions when it may be impossible. A true broadcast service, giving constant field strength at all times over the whole globe, would be invaluable, not to say indispensable, in a world society.

Unsatisfactory though the telephone and telegraph position is, that of television is far worse, since ionospheric transmission cannot be employed at all. The service area of a television station, even on a very good site, is only about 100 miles across. To cover a small country such as Great Britain would require a network of transmitters, connected by coaxial lines, wave guides of VHF relay links. A recent theoretical study (by C. W. Hansell, *Proc. I.R.E.*, 33, March 1945)[*] has shown that such a system would require repeaters at intervals of 50 miles or less. A system of this kind could provide television coverage, at a very considerable cost, over the whole of a small country. It would be out of the question to provide a large continent with such a service, and only the main centers of population could be included in the network.

The problem is equally serious when an attempt is made to link television services in different parts of the globe. A relay chain several thousand miles long would cost millions, and transoceanic services would still be impossible. Similar considerations apply to the provision of wide-band frequency modulation and other services, such as high-

[*] C. W. Hansell, then with the Radio Corporation of America Laboratories, in *Proceedings of the Institute of Radio Engineers*, New York.

speed facsimile which are by their nature restricted to ultra-high frequencies.

Clarke saw clearly that the way out of all this was "extraterrestrial relays" in orbit around the earth. But the year was 1945, and any such idea had to be advanced with caution. He continued: "Many may consider the solution proposed in this discussion too farfetched to be taken very seriously. Such an attitude is unreasonable, as everything envisaged here is a logical extension of developments in the last ten years—in particular the perfection of the long-range rocket of which V-2 was the prototype." He then quoted an unspecified German source stating that the establishment of a satellite system would be "possible within 50 to 100 years."

This last sentence shows the dangers of technological predictions. Between the appearance of Arthur C. Clarke's article and the first transmission via Telstar precisely 16½ years have gone by.

ꙮ   Early Planning

As the working elements of the worldwide communications network, Clarke proposed 3 satellites in 24-hour orbit, circling the earth over the equator and positioned over the intersection of the equator and the following longitudes:

30° East for serving Africa and Europe (this position is somewhat to the west of the western shore of Lake Victoria);
150° East for serving eastern Asia, Australia, and so on (this is over the western tip of New Guinea);
90° West for serving the Americas (this is over the southern portion of the Gulf of Mexico).

Since the main ingredients of the scheme, the large rocket and short-wave technology, were both in existence when Clarke wrote this article, a program for establishing his extraterrestrial relays could have been initiated then. True, the rockets were not

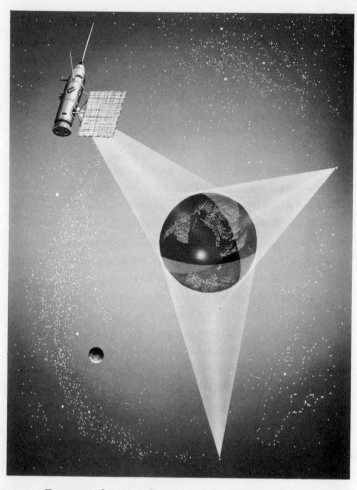

Drawing of a 3-satellite system in 24-hour orbit for global
communications coverage.

yet big enough and short-wave technology still had to be developed further, but the basic means for reaching the goal were there.

Improving the rockets and radio techniques both took time and nothing was said about communication satellites for a number of years. About 1953 various scientists investigated a number of specific points, such as the most suitable wavelength or wavelengths for such application and the question of the most suitable orbit. For example, Robert P. Haviland, now with General Electric's Missile and Space Division, calculated the area a communication satellite could serve even before Vanguard I was fired. Condensed, his table reads as follows:

Table 8
AREA SERVICEABLE BY A COMMUNICATION SATELLITE

Altitude of satellite above sea level (MILES)	Distance of satellite from the earth's limb (MILES)	Vision arc (MILES)	Percentage of total area of earth served by satellite
257	1,445	1,400	17
620	2,310	2,100	25
1,210	3,350	2,800	32
4,000	6,920	4,200	43
22,300	26,800	5,800	49.5

The first column in this table needs no explanation. The second column gives the distance to the satellite from a point on the ground for which the satellite is at the horizon. The third column shows the maximum distance between two points on earth, both of which have the satellite on the horizon. It can be seen that neither the distance between two such points nor the area served increase much between satellite altitudes of 4,000 and 22,300 miles, but the latter has the advantage of pro-

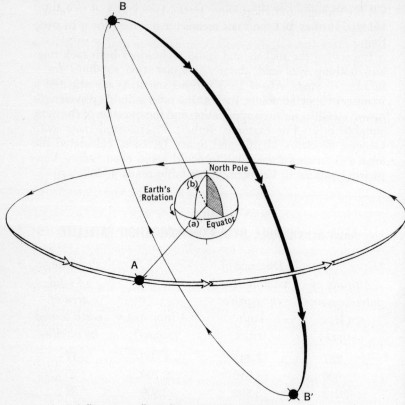

A "stationary" satellite over the equator.

ducing the synchronous and therefore apparently motionless satellite. The principle of the "stationary" satellite is illustrated in the above drawing.

Satellite A [the equatorial synchronous orbit] is rotating in an orbit parallel to the equator and at a velocity such that point (a) on the earth is always directly under it on the line joining the satellite with the *center* of the earth. Similarly Satellite B, also rotating about the *center* of the earth once in 24 hours, will be over point (b) at the time shown. However, it will not remain over point (b). Twelve hours later the satellite will be in orbit at point B' over a point on the earth in the Southern Hemisphere. To an observer on the earth the satellite would appear to move from north to south and back each time it completes an orbit. While not remaining stationary over a single point on the earth, it would retrace the same earth track once each day.*

The equatorial synchronous orbit is significant because it permits stations on the surface of the earth to install directional antennas that need to move very little in order always to be pointing at the satellite. Fixed structures are much less expensive and less complicated to construct, and consequently the possibility of their use would promote the development of a system by small-user nations much more rapidly and widely than would be true if the structures they might build were required to search out satellites in random orbits.

Although a satellite in synchronous orbit over the equator appears to remain stationary, there are substantial advantages to be obtained from other controlled orbits. If 3 satellites are placed in an orbit so that they rotate about the earth once in 8 hours they will trace the same earth track on each third orbit as they will make precisely 3 orbits in the 24-hour day. This permits a ground station to be constructed that can follow the satellite by moving its antenna in the same direction each time it is used. Thus it

---

* *Communication Satellites: Technical, Economic and International Developments;* Staff Report, prepared for the use of the Committee on Aeronautical and Space Sciences, United States Senate (87th Congress, 2d Session), February 25, 1962, p. 38.

will not be so difficult to share radio-frequency use as it would be if the antenna were to be permitted to search all over the sky. A similar configuration of 4 satellites in 6-hour orbits would accomplish the same end result.

The "subsynchronous" orbit satellites [all those at altitudes less than 22,300 miles] could be of importance in those instances in which it is essential to communicate with the polar regions. The 24-hour equatorial synchronous satellite could not be "seen" directly from either pole, yet the polar regions are of substantial military significance.

Lower-altitude orbits have advantages under certain circumstances, even though more complicated ground tracking installations are required. They are easier to attain. Under favorable conditions some frequency-sharing benefit appears possible. The radio-frequency spectrum is a limited resource, and consequently it is desirable to share it as much as possible. Low-altitude satellites are within sight of a smaller geographical area on earth. This makes it possible to use the same radio frequencies on more satellites simultaneously. Special station-keeping engineering would, however, be required if the satellites were to be placed in subsynchronous orbits . . . [to] avoid . . . the possibility of having overlapping service areas. Long-distance communications might require more than one "hop," * using more frequencies. "Hand-over"

---

* One "hop" refers to a transmission from one ground station via satellite to another; hence several "hops" would require as many satellites. The "hand-over" technique is needed when a satellite is setting while active. In this case, the beam on the setting satellite is augmented by another beam, carrying the same message or set of messages to another satellite overhead, so that there is no interruption of the message flow at the receiving end.

Drawing of a "stationary" communication satellite in 24-hour orbit.

techniques for handling low-orbit satellites may be complicated and require more frequencies than those in synchronous orbits.[*]

The Telstar satellite is not in a synchronous orbit; it describes a rather eccentric elliptical orbit with a perigee of 593 miles and an apogee of 3,503 miles. Its orbital period is 157.8 minutes, thus the satellite is only occasionally in an orbital position so that it can be used for transmitting between Andover, Maine, the American terminal, and the two west European terminals in Cornwall, England, and at Pleurmeur-Badow, in France.

[*] *Communication Satellites, op. cit.,* p. 40.

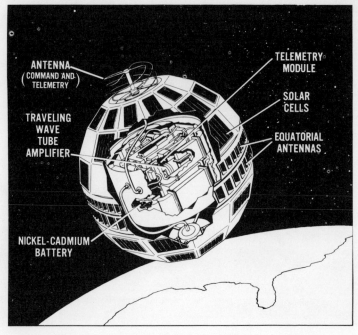

Cut-away drawing showing equipment carried by Bell System's Telstar.

But it must be emphasized that Telstar is purely experimental. The American Telephone and Telegraph Company, which purchased a Thor-Delta rocket from the government to put Telstar into orbit, seems to favor, at least for the present, a number of satellites in a comparatively low orbit. These would require the hand-over techniques mentioned. Most space scientists feel that the ultimate goal, however, will be the 3-satellite system in the 24-hour orbit. In fact, NASA has contracted with the Hughes Aircraft Company, Culver City, California, for the development of a satellite called "Syncom." The first of these satellites, whose launching has been proposed for 1963, will carry just 1 telephone-channel relay in order to make it as light as possible. One of the reasons for making it light is that it takes a great deal of rocket thrust to carry a satellite to

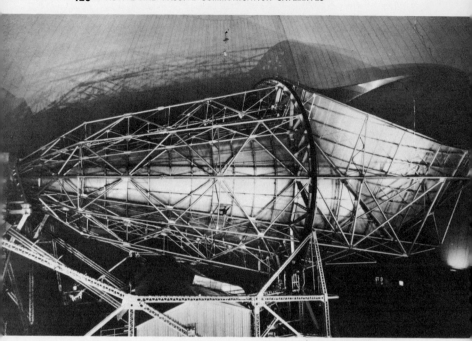

380-ton horn antenna at Andover, Maine, used to transmit
signals to and receive signals from Telstar.

the comparatively distant 24-hour orbit. A "comsat," weighing
a ton or more, would have to wait for the heavy Saturn booster
to place it that far out; in the meantime the system can be
tested, using a Thor-Delta rocket as the booster, if the satellite
is light enough. The first Syncom is designed to weigh just 75
pounds, considerably less than the 170-pound Telstar.

⋈   Active and Passive Communication Satellites

There can be some argument as to whether the Atlas rocket
orbited on December 18, 1958, under the name of Project

Bell System's Andover, Maine, satellite-communication station. The building in the foreground houses equipment to operate the horn antenna in the dome in the background.

SCORE should be considered the first communication satellite or not. A tape recorder in the rocket broadcast a Christmas message from President Eisenhower that had been recorded prior to take off. But while it was possible to erase the tape and record another message for broadcasting from space, Project SCORE was, strictly speaking, not a communication satellite. No communication from one point on the ground to another

(*Opposite*) Steerable dish aerial of the United Kingdom Satellite station, Cornwall, England, used to receive signals from U.S.-launched communication satellites.

point on the ground was provided by SCORE; it was a test of the feasibility of broadcasting from space.

The first satellite definitely falling under the definition of a communication satellite was the 100-foot aluminized mylar plastic-film balloon Echo I, put into orbit on August 12, 1960. Echo I did precisely what is implied in its name, it acted as a reflector for radio signals. This type of "comsat"—one that merely reflects a signal but does not amplify it—is known as a *passive satellite*.

The distinction between passive satellites that reflect transmissions from the ground and active satellites that retransmit such received signals is a signfiicant one. The active satellites are designed to amplify the received signals. Such amplification greatly reduces the need for extremely sensitive receiving equipment on the ground. In addition, it means that receivers having a certain degree of sensitivity can be used to receive signals having a broader bandwidth than could be received satisfactorily by reflection from a passive satellite.

All the advantages do not lie with the active satellites, however. The Echo satellite will reflect the signals over a wider range of frequencies than will active satellites proposed for construction under present research-and-development programs and is more reliable.

A current problem in development of communication satellites is to provide adequate power for active satellites. Passive satellites, of course, do not require power sources, and this constitutes an advantage. As has been noted above in connection with active satellites in 24-hour synchronous equatorial orbits, the satellites must be at such a distance from the earth—22,300 miles—that the returned signal is weak compared with that from satellites from

Echo I undergoing an inflation test in its hangar.

An Echo satellite in its canister. After launching the canister separates and the plastic Echo sphere orbits about 1,000 miles from the earth.

lower orbits. This deficiency would be expected, of course, to be even more serious were a passive satellite put into a 24-hour synchronous orbit. Because of the electrical reliability of passive satellites, however, a 24-hour synchronous passive satellite is an attractive system. In order to enhance the returned signal it might be possible to construct a reflector that would concentrate the reflected signal in the direction from which it came; that is, toward the earth. This was, in fact, suggested again recently by Berl D. Levenson, of Aerospace Corporation, at the Aerospace Technology Symposium, September 4, 1961. Mr. Levenson proposed a passive 24-hour synchronous satellite using antennae in which "the relationship between the direction of incidence and the direction of high-gain reflection is independent of the attitude of the reflector about any axis." He would use a combination antenna consisting of plane and conical arrays.

Mr. Levenson also suggested a second type of reflector in which the direction of incidence and the direction of high-gain reflection is independent of the attitude of the reflector about an axis parallel to the earth' spin axis. Such a reflector might consist of 3 mutually intersecting conducting planes.

Another speaker at the Aerospace Symposium, Dr. S. G. Lutz, of Hughes Research Laboratories, argued for an active satellite system, stating that a passive satellite-communications system would not be economically competitive with high-capacity active systems (except for those systems intended to satisfy special military requirements), because of the greater terminal [ground station] costs.*

* *Communication Satellites, op. cit.,* p. 37.

Spin test of a small Hughes Aircraft communication satellite.

The exchange of opinions between Levenson and Lutz was based, as pointed out by Dr. Lutz, on the fact that communication satellites, the prime civilian application of satellite techniques, also have a military value. It is probably correct to state that the satellites for civilian uses *must* be active to do their job properly, while the military, operating during high emergencies, might well rely on passive satellites.

⚎ In the Event of War

It might be assumed that an enemy, as part of a nuclear attack, would use interceptor missiles to destroy existing (active) communication satellites. Simultaneously, normal long-range radio communication would be disturbed, if not rendered impossible, as a by-product of the attack.

Accompanying an atomic explosion is a disturbance of the ionosphere with the result that the ionosphere may not perform its usual function of reflecting radio rays back to earth for a number of hours. When this occurs, long-distance communications which depend upon that particular portion of the ionosphere may be disrupted. It is easy to understand how devastating this could be. If alternate means of communication must be found, communication satellites (assuming they were not destroyed in an attack) could be a very attractive solution to the problem because they are not dependent upon the ionosphere.

One of the first evidences of the space radio "blackout" phenomena was in August 1958. At that time the Atomic Energy Commission reported:

On August 1 and 12, 1958, nuclear warheads were detonated in missiles over Johnston Island in the Pacific. These detonations were accompanied by impressive visual displays seen over wide areas, leading observers to the opinion that the detonations took place at very high altitudes. These displays were even seen on Samoa, some 2,000 miles from Johnston Island.

The visual displays were accompanied by disruptive effects on radio communications. Specifically, most commercial communiation systems operating on the high-frequency (about 5 to 25 megacycles) bands in the Pacific noted substantial disturbances. Most links within a few hundred miles of Johnston Island experienced "outages" for as long as several hours, at various times over a period of a day. In general, the effects on high-frequency communication links appear to have been quite similar to the effects produced by giant solar flares.*

With both existing active satellites and ionosphere eliminated, the answer would be passive satellites that could be put into low orbits quickly, using, for example, solid-fuel Scout rockets as carriers. The possibility of using a rocket that merely climbs high enough in vertical flight, as a passive communication satellite, has also been investigated.

But the main need for communication satellites is the (by contrast) pleasant fact that the growth of civilian long-range communications causes problems in the ordinary channels of communication. One might say that the communications needs at present are such that communication satellites would have to be created in a hurry if the idea did not already exist. Since long-range communications rely on the ability of the ionosphere to reflect radio waves, the sunspot cycle (the dark spots that appear from time to time on the sun's surface), which can disrupt such communication, acquires commercial importance for the first time in history.

* The extract is from *Meteorological Satellites;* Staff Report prepared for the use of the Committee on Aeronautical and Space Sciences, United States Senate, by the Library of Congress (87th Congress, 2d Session), March 29, 1962, p. 134. Reprinted. with the above material, in *Communication Satellites, op. cit.,* p. 27.

⚏ The Sunspot Cycle

Cycles are about 11 years long, and the number of sunspots rise to a maximum relatively fast during that period but then decrease slowly to a minimum. The last sunspot maximum, reached in 1958–59, was higher than at any time since systematic observations commenced in 1849. It is expected that the minimum will occur about April 1965, although it may occur as early as January 1963. However, the high-frequency broadcasting bands are greatly congested under the most favorable circumstances. With the decrease in number of sunspots, the high-frequency limit of usable spectrum for long-distance communications also decreases. This squeezes services that have been using higher frequencies into the lower portions of the spectrum, further increasing the congestion. . . .

Influence of the sun upon the ionosphere is of two types, one beneficial and the other not. The number of sunspots appears to correlate with the degree of ultraviolet radiation from the sun; and this radiation determines the general level of ionization, that property of the ionosphere causing the radio waves to be reflected when they reach it. The higher the degree of ionization, the higher is the upper limit of radio frequencies which may be reflected.

On the other hand, corpuscular and X radiation from the sun associated with solar flares is harmful to long-distance radio communication because the high-energy particles cause turbulence in the ionosphere, upsetting its reflective properties and increasing its absorption of radio waves normally used for long-distance communication.

The high-energy corpuscles are trapped in the earth's magnetic field, travel to the poles, and are responsible for the auroras. They also travel much more slowly from the sun than does the ultraviolet radiation. This is evident when a solar flare associated with a large sunspot is seen. Radio communication may be enhanced for a short time immediately afterward as the extra ultraviolet radiation arives and then be destroyed completely as the slower-moving corpuscular radiation arrives.[*]

Ⓜ Intercontinental Communication at Present

Congress, looking into the matter of civilian long-range communication, received an impressive amount of testimony, not only about the desirability of communication satellites, but also about the urgency of the problem.

Dr. Henri Busignies of the International Telephone & Telegraph Corporation testified before the House Committee on Science and Astronautics on May 9, 1961:

A preliminary accounting of all existing facilities indicates the present-day transmission capacity between the United States and Europe is not in excess of 180 voice channels. It is fair to assume that, at the presently planned expansion, the number of voice channels available will not exceed 300 within the next 2 years.

It should be noted that the peak density of traffic flow extends over only a few hours a day, because of the difference in time zones between New York and Europe. During this busy period, the present circuits are overloaded and the waiting time can be excessive.

[*] *Communication Satellites, op. cit.*, pp. 26–27.

The number of telephone messages handled between the United States and all areas of the world has steadily increased over the past few years. For all toll calls within a country, 6 to 8 per cent increase per year is the usual figure.

For transatlantic calls, a 15 per cent increase per year is the present standard planning figure, but it must be recognized that this planning is intended to err on the conservative side. In almost all cases all cable-grade facilities have been fully loaded with traffic within 90 to 150 days after they become available. Thus no one has any measure of how much potential traffic is being kept from realization by the lack of facilities.

It should be emphasized that a substantial increase can be expected only as a result of additional facilities that provide fully dependable cable quality as it is expected that the satellite communications would furnish. For example, the introduction of the first Atlantic cable in 1956 caused a 90 per cent increase in the number of calls.

Based on the present-day traffic distribution, the number of channels required by 1965 between the United States and the major countries in the area covered by a mid-Atlantic satellite is of the order of 1,000. This is in addition to the present capabilities of cable and radio systems.

The best estimates available show channel requirements for both the Atlantic and the Pacific (including South America and Africa in the Atlantic requirements) of the order of 2,000 by 1970, and of 4,000 to 6,000 by 1980.

This last figure is several thousand channels above the present and expected cable capacity. . . .

There seems to be little doubt that satellite communications are the solution for the additional channel requirements that are developing now and during the next two decades.

Mr. James Dingman of the American Telephone & Telegraph Company testified before the House Committee on Science and Astronautics, giving his company's views on how a communication-satellite system would serve civil communication needs:

> Such a system would also be uniquely suited to expanding service to the developing areas of the world. It would provide added security and reliability, both by making available alternate routes and by affording direct access to areas now reached only by means either of radio, which is subject to sunspot interference, or by intermediate land links through other countries. The satellite system would even be flexible enough to permit use of portable ground stations to give access on short notice to trouble spots around the world.
>
> The demand for additional, more versatile oversea communications is growing tremendously. The volume of oversea telephone calls is expected to increase from 4 million in 1960 to 20 million in 1970 and nearly 100 million by 1980. This means that oversea telephone circuits will have to be increased from the some 500 we have today to about 12,000 in 1980. The international telegraph business is also growing rapidly.

Among the other responsible organizations that have made serious attempts at estimating potential communication-satellite traffic is the General Electric Company. In its filing of March 1, 1961, before the Federal Communications Commission in connection with docket 13522, GE used an operational research approach as follows:

> The demand for these services is related to total demand for communications, and to economic and technical comparisons between existing services and the new satellite services.

For the relay services, an estimate of worldwide traffic, and of the existing capability has been prepared. This is shown in summary chart form on the opposite page. In this figure, the width of the line joining two continents is estimated demand for communication between those continents for the period around 1970. Shading within the line shows existing [1960] capacity. . . .

This study indicates that the North Atlantic path will have the most traffic for many years. However, there are 8 other routes of major importance, and 5 others of appreciable importance.

The existing capacity has been estimated by summing the capacity of existing telephone and telegraph radio and cable circuits, using a 3-minute telephone conversation as a unit.

Comparison of the 1970 demand and existing facilities shows that even the heavily served North Atlantic route will require capacity increase by about a 2 to 1 factor. Capacity on the remaining routes must increase by a greater factor, on the order of 5 to 1, although, of course, the absolute magnitude of the increase may be small. However, it should be noted that the expected traffic on several routes will equal or exceed the present North Atlantic traffic. This makes consideration of the world traffic system a necessity.

Estimates of the total traffic across the North Atlantic have been prepared by extrapolation of traffic for the past 40 years. This indicates that the expected number of equivalent message units for this path is 6×10^6 units per year in 1970. The traffic on the other paths is easily obtained by multiplication.

Estimates of the traffic for the period around 1980 have also been made. They show essentially the same pattern as for 1970, with a slight increase in traffic from the newly developing areas. Total traffic is estimated to be between 3 and 5 times the 1970 traffic, based on current growth ratios.

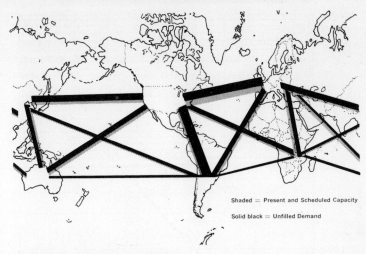

Shaded = Present and Scheduled Capacity

Solid black = Unfilled Demand

Estimated demand for intercontinental communication service.

The satisfaction of this demand by means of long-distance high-frequency radio techniques is impossible, due to lack of suitable spectrum space. Microwave relay of the current type is also not possible except at inordinate expense. This indicates that the demand must be satisfied by high quality submarine cables, or by satellite relay.

William Meckling, an economist with the Rand Corporation, has attempted to analyze prospective increase in demand for overseas telephone calls during the next 2 decades. He writes: [1]

Since the depression of the 1930's oversea telephone communications have grown steadily and rapidly. The figure on the next page shows the annual totals of inbound and outbound oversea messages for the United States for the period 1930–59. During those 30 years the

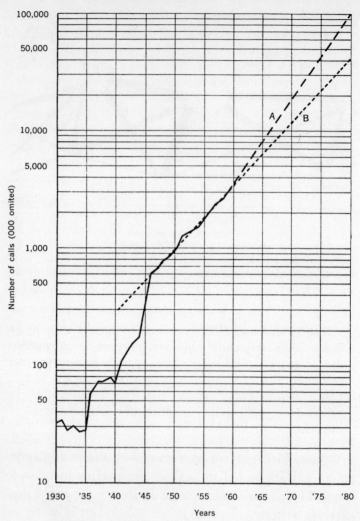

Overseas telephone calls per year to and from the United States for the period 1930–80.

number of messages increased by a factor of 100. In the last 10 years the volume of messages roughly tripled. As is evident from the regular slope of the line, the rate of growth has been remarkably constant since 1946. If that same growth rate persists, the volume of oversea messages will reach 10 to 12 million by 1970 and around 40 million by 1980. The dotted line B in the chart opposite is based on a growth rate like that of the postwar period. The dashed line A is based on a substantially higher growth rate, which predicts 20 million or so messages in 1970 and 100 million by 1980. A corresponds roughly to the assumption of a 15 per cent annual increase. . . .

The Lockheed Aircraft Corporation had a "Telecommunications Satellite Business Planning Study," prepared by Booz, Allen & Hamilton, management consultants. In commenting on the more rapid rate of growth of telephone calls than the rate of private foreign investment, the study states that "this divergence is at least partly due to the increased capacity and higher quality of voice transmission afforded by the several transoceanic cables installed. . . ." The fading and other difficulties experienced with conventional high-frequency international radiotelephone service are well known. The new service by way of communication satellites is expected to avoid this and provide service of a quality comparable with that over the new cables.[*]

This extensive testimony from various types of businesses certainly testifies to the need for communication satellites, and the performance of Telstar has shown that the electronics problems can be considered largely solved. And, as has been mentioned, a prototype of the "syncom" satellite system is about

[*] *Communication Satellites, op. cit.,* pp. 64–67.

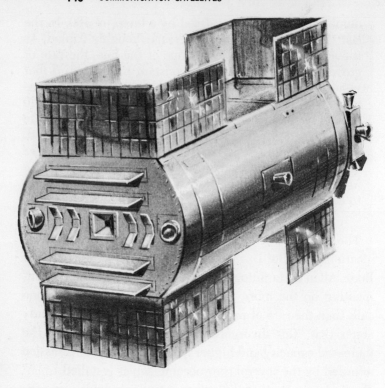

Drawing of Lockheed's proposed communication satellite.

ready to be launched. The Saturn booster will furnish the lifting power to put large syncoms into their orbit.

 In the Interest of Peace

But not all the problems have been solved. There are others, political in nature—using the word "politics" in its largest meaning—that stand in the way of establishing an international communications network using artificial satellites.

Douglas Aircraft Company's concept of a "comsat" telephone satellite.

The close link between U.S. military and civilian space programs may cause concern among foreign governments that U.S. peaceful applications may have military implications. Senator John Stennis pointed out that [2]

. . . Our overinsistence on classifying our space activities as either "military" or "peaceful" has exposed us to unnecessary international political problems. It gives

Bell Telephone Laboratories technicians prepare a 34-inch experimental forerunner of Telstar for transmission experiments.

the Soviets a convenient focus for attack upon our most vital program.

Dr. Edward C. Welsh, executive secretary of the National Aeronautics and Space Council, also spoke of the misunderstandings that may develop through an attempt, artificially, to equate military and nonmilitary space activity as nonpeaceful and peaceful. In speaking before the

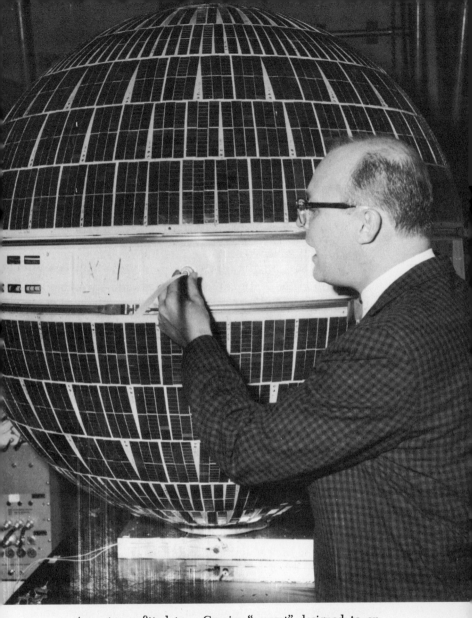

An antenna fitted to a Courier "comsat" designed to exchange 340,000 words in a 5-minute period of its orbit.

American Astronautical Society in Washington, D.C., on January 17, 1962, he said:

> There are some well-intentioned people who would draw a line—in fact, a barrier—between what they call peaceful uses and nonpeaceful uses of outer space.
>
> As I have done so many times in the past, I again emphasize that it is our national policy that all our space efforts are peaceful. We do not have a division between peaceful and nonpeaceful objectives for space. Rather, we have space missions to help keep the peace and space missions to improve our ability to live well in peace. . . .
>
> In the National Aeronautics and Space Act, which established the National Aeronautics and Space Council and the NASA, the Congress made it explicit that all activities in space should be devoted to peaceful purposes. The law affirms that some of those peaceful purposes should be the responsibility of the NASA and some should be the responsibility of the Defense Department, with the President determining which such agency has the responsibility for and the direction of each of those peaceful space activities. I add that the act recognizes that other agencies also have space responsibilities. Those responsibilities are likewise peaceful in intent.*

Of course, even the strongest statements will not convince those persons who have made up their minds to be suspicious. Such suspicions wither away from lack of nourishment, and after American communication satellites have performed their tasks for many years, they will simply be accepted as existing—the question of their military implications will fade away.

The second set of political complications concerns the ownership of communication satellites. Other countries do not have this problem. In Europe, the electric telegraph was invented at a time when no private investor thought it lucrative, while

---

* *Communication Satellites, op. cit.,* p. 72.

the various national post offices considered it useful for their purposes. In this way, as the telegraph system developed, it became a section of the post office. When the telephone was invented, a precedent had been established, and it, too, was incorporated as a department of the post office. Radio, and still later, television followed the same path; in most European countries they became departments of the government, usually subsections of the post office.

In the United States, the means of communication are privately owned and are merely supervised by a government agency. It seems unlikely that this established system (it might with equal justification be referred to as a national habit) of private ownership can be reversed at this late date. But in whatever manner the problem of private versus public ownership may be resolved, it will not interfere with the advent of the communication satellites.

They are badly needed.

REFERENCES

1. Meckling, William, "Economic Potential of Communication Satellites," *Science*, June 16, 1961, p. 1890.
2. *Congressional Record*, Sept. 26, 1961, p. 19969.

5 Do the Russians Plan a Separate Communications System?

IF FOREIGN governments are wondering about the possible military implications of our satellite programs, we are similarly concerned about their activities in this area.

There is considerable speculation regarding U.S.S.R. development of communication satellites. It is the optimistic belief in some quarters that the Soviet bloc has done little in this area of space research.

The suggestion that we will outdistance the U.S.S.R. in communication satellites was expressed by Dr. Herbert York, former Director of Defense Research and Engineering, Department of Defense: [1]

I don't know if they have a communication satellite. They show no evidence of it. I am sure we will overtake them in these objectives.

Senator Magnuson, in a review of the potentialities of communication satellites before the American Rocket Society, referred to speculation concerning Soviet capabilities [at one of the Society's meetings at the New York Coliseum, October 9–15, 1961]:

> I think it is important, . . . that the United States anticipate Soviet Russia or any other unfriendly nation in providing satellite communication services, particularly television, to the uncommitted peoples and the underdeveloped areas of the world.
>
> Witnesses at the Commerce Committee hearings suggested that this can only be considered as a long-term objective. I am not convinced. Technology in the space sciences and in telecommunications has made spectacular advances in the past few months, and is accelerating.

Referring further to a Brookings Institution report for NASA he quoted the following: [2]

> The U.S.S.R. may also be planning a communication satellite system. The complications of adjusting the various systems involved in the shift in communications methods might possibly be fewer in countries where the presently utilized systems are publicly owned. Thus Russia, with its different economic and political philosophy, might be able to move ahead rapidly to meet the technological requirements. If it becomes clearly evident that Russia is planning a communication satellite system, there will surely be additional pressures on Government to act quickly and decisively in forwarding the U.S. efforts.

Others have expressed similar views on this subject and fear that delays may result in the United States's inability to be successful in winning the ideological contest with the Soviet Union.

ᙁ Gravitational Waves—
a Russian Speculation

There has been reference to the possible development of communication satellites by [Russian] journalists writing for domestic consumption, but that may only be a means of pacifying the curiosity of the people concerning this field. One such instance was an "Interview at Readers' Request: Space Radio Communications," by Professor A. Kugushev, doctor of technical sciences, reported to have appeared in the May 27 [1961] issue of *Izvestia*.

There was a radioteletype Tass broadcast in English from Moscow to Europe on April 24, 1960, which allowed the Western powers to gather a small amount of data on a U.S.S.R. scientific study pertaining to technical aspects of space communications. Vladimir Fok, a winner of the Lenin Prize for research in quantum theory, indicated that gravitational waves [the existence of which is highly doubtful, to say the least] might be used for communication between earth and spaceships.

A bold idea for the use of gravitation as a means of communication that would rival radio is suggested by a group of Soviet engineers in an article in Izvestia's Sunday supplement. They write that gravitational oscillations [similar to?] electromagnetic oscillations which form the basis of radio could be used for wireless communication. These oscillations could be produced by making any body rotate, or simply move.

Academician Vladimir Fok, . . . has calculated that in rotating around the sun, Jupiter emits gravitational oscillations of 450 watts. The power of the gravitational waves rapidly grows with the increase in the frequency of oscillations of [sic] the number of revolutions. It is, for instance, sufficient to increase the number of revolutions 10 times to produce an increase in the power of the gravitational emission by 1 million times.

Modern radio technique, using superconductivity [virtual absence of resistance to current flow at very low temperatures], can make electrons oscillate with a frequency of billions per second. Such an electronic "graviotransmitter" would be able to produce a power of dozens of watts. This device could be used as a "gravioreceiver" for transforming gravitational oscillations into ordinary radio signals.

The use of gravitational waves would make it possible to establish communication through earth, water, and the ionosphere, since they can penetrate through media which are absolutely impenetrable to radio waves. Gravitational communication would, for instance, enable us to talk with miners. A radiolocator based on gravitational waves could investigate deep-lying earth strata. Gravitational waves will also make it possible to maintain contact between the earth and spaceships, which become inaccessible to radio on reaching ionic clouds.

Some indication of where the U.S.S.R. stands in demonstrations of ability in space transmission control was reported at the American Rocket Society meeting in Washington in December 1960: [3]

Since radio transmissions from positions in space have effects which go beyond the activities of any one nation, the requirement that transmitter and orbital commands be used in connection with all active communication satellites must be applied to each nation which undertakes space activities. The Soviet Union is the only other world power which at present has a space capability. For purposes of comparison it is interesting to note what, if anything, the Russians have been doing about controlling space transmissions.

It is no secret that the Soviet Union has recently demonstrated in connection with Spacecraft I (1960 Epsilon) [which is usually called Sputnik IV; the spacecraft designation is not international but Russian] and Spacecraft II (1960 Lamda) [Sputnik V] that it possessed the ability to control a vehicle's orbit. Lunik II (1959 Theta) indicated a capacity for a high degree of control over the attitude of a vehicle once orbit is achieved. While the Russians have not released much detail concerning their present ground-to-space vehicle control activities, informed opinion concedes that Russia does possess the ability to exercise a high degree of transmitter and orbital control. (Interview [by Mr. Haley] with Col. Paul Nadler, ARPA [Advanced Research Projects Agency], Washington, D.C., November 22, 1960.) The indications are, however, that the capability mentioned above has but recently been acquired.

This ability to control satellites in orbit is of significance in connection with planned orbital rendezvous of one satellite with another. Although of marginal interest as far as communication satellites are concerned at the moment, such a capability is of great interest and concern with regard to other space uses and the ultimate capability of retrieval and repair of malfunctioning communication satellites.

Another assessment of where we stand vis-à-vis the Soviet Union in the space race was provided by Dr. Edward C. Welsh, executive secretary of the National Aeronautics and Space Council. He posed the question of where we stood in comparison with the U.S.S.R. and answered it as follows, including reference to space communications: [4]

> . . . the following would seem to be a reasonable capsuled comparison. The United States leads in the number of successful launches by a margin of more than 3 to 1. We also have obtained a wider range of scientific information about space and have made more progress in applying space technology in the weather, navigation and communications fields. . . . It is clear, however, that the Soviets are ahead in the single most critical aspect of the race, the ability to put heavy payloads into space.

He said that we could not expect the Soviets to wait for us to catch up in our efforts to overcome the booster lag.

⩜ Russian Views on Space Communication

As far as Communist publicity regarding their interest in space communications is concerned, at least 3 articles are reported to have appeared in 1960 in the Communist bloc press. Written by a Soviet scientist, they mentioned the development of satellite communications. "A Glance into the Future of Our Science," by Alexander Nesmeyanov, president of the Soviet Academy of Sciences, appeared on January 1, 1960 [in Russian newspapers]. In it he stated:

> Soviet science is planning the use of satellite and meteorological service and radio communications.

In May 1960 Nesmeyanov wrote, in *Tekhnika Molodezhi* ("Technology for the Youth"):

> . . . Soviet scientists were planning to use manmade earth sateliltes in meteorology and radio communications.

Later, for East German readers, he wrote in *Neues Deutschland* ("New Germany"), on December 11, 1960, that:

> Soviet scientists are working on plans to utilize satellites for meteorological and radio services.

The report further states that M. V. Keldysh, who was president of the Soviet Academy of Sciences in 1961, made a report to the All Union Conference of Research Workers, held in June 1961, in which he stated:

> a priority of the highest importance is given to artificial earth satellites in solving a number of economic problems, observations performed through the use of satellites would create a radical improvement in weather forecasting, radio communications, and solar utilization. The use of communications . . . satellites for relay services would revolutionize communications and television services.

As early as 1953 scientists in the U.S.S.R. were discussing the use of a Sputnik for television:[5]

> Using a sputnik to boost enormously the present range of television broadcasts was suggested by Prof. S. Katayev in December 1957. He recalled that such novel employment of a satellite had attracted the attention of television experts for a long time. It was discussed in detail at a 1953 conference of Russian scientists and

technicians. In the West, in fact, the idea had been broached and argued even earlier, before 1953 [Bell Laboratories in the United States]. But the Russians, even when agreeing that Americans might have thought of it first, say that in the early 1950's the implementation of the idea seemed remote, if not entirely implausible, for the main postulate—a sputnik—was not as yet in its orbit.

Beginning with the sputnik era, however, the prospect became wholly realistic, and, in Katayev's prediction [Prof. S. Katayev in *Isvestia*], Red sputniks of the very near future may become just such needed relay and boosting stations to make television truly far flung in "such great territories as possessed, say, by our nation." With the help of a large sputnik and the necessary equipment, and sent up to a height considerably greater than reached by the first Russian satellites, "Moscow television programs could easily be relayed not alone to any point of the Soviet Union, but also far beyond its borders—to China and Antarctica, for instance." Such a television-relaying sputnik will have to be sent up in the area of the Equator, where it would be made to stay and "wander slowly in a limited space as if 'hanging' over one of the regions of the Equator," so that the television signals, relayed by its antenna, could be received anywhere and everywhere on the surface of the hemisphere facing it.

Other predictions of television by communication satellite were cited by a corresponding member of the Soviet Academy of Sciences:[6]

Communication by words and pictures can be tremendously expanded and facilitated when man embarks on his outer-space career. Radio and television broadcasts of the spacemen's future day will be stepped up, not alone by special sputniks to be sent up expressly for this purpose, but also through other means. Take, for instance, ultrashort radio waves as reflected by meteorite trails: they, too, can be used for man's radio signals over long distances. So declares A. L. Mints, a corresponding member of the Soviet Academy of Sciences. He maintains that a method of such communication has already been worked out, but admits he does not know how practical it may prove.

He also asserts that, instead of using such meteorite-trail radio waves, a radio-wave reflecting "mirror" can be created artificially "high in the sky" by shooting a rocket into the upper reaches of the atmosphere. The rocket, at the highest point of its trajectory, releases— as dust—a quantity of metallic potassium. The resulting cloud of the thinnest possible powder becomes ionized under the effect of sunrays and acquires its capacity of reflecting radio waves, thus replacing the meteorite trails. Such a cloud can last 45 minutes and may be used for radio communications for periods longer than is now possible without aid of the artificial "mirror" made by the potassium-sprinkling rocket.

On August 13, 1961, an article is reported to have appeared in *Pravda* written by Professor Ari Shternfel'd, who is a Soviet winner of the International Prize in Astronautics. In this article he told of a plan for launching an equatorial synchronous communication satellite at a height of 35,800 kilometers [22,300 miles]. The satellites, which would be several tons in weight, are heavier than those currently being considered in this country. Furthermore, the satellites would be assembled in orbit and the last stage of the rocket could be used to create a multiton satellite station. The Soviet scientist previously, on several other occasions, publicized his views on the assembling of satellites in orbit, and the use of space platforms.

More recently, Mr. H. F. Clesner prepared a memorandum in which he mentioned an interview in the Soviet press with a technical designer of spacecraft: [7]

The chief designer of the Vostok spaceships stated in an interview in *Krasnaya Zveda* on October 11, 1961, that the creation in the near future of satellites for relaying television and communication signals and for the purposes of navigation and meteorology and other scientific tasks of economic significance is technically feasible. An important stage in the development of satellite flights would be the creation at various altitudes of permanent orbital stations which would hang forever above the earth (a synchronous system).

Further, he disclosed that a system for safely getting service and control personnel to such stations and back to earth may be already worked out. He pointed out that the most technically feasible way would be to create such stations while in orbit around the earth, using materials which would have nothing in common with ordinary construction materials.

The chief designer usually is a key personage in the Soviet technology hierarchy for he probably has the responsibility in this instance of carrying out the task of constructing such a vehicle. He is the manager of the program with operational control over enterprises, plants, and personnel. It is his job to deliver.

These words of their high officials cannot be discounted as mere puffing. For it is a fact that key Soviet personages, such as Nesmeyanov used similar words as the chief designer's in the period preceding the development and flight of Sputnik I and Yuri Gagarin's manned orbital flight.

One of the U.S.S.R.'s most outstanding missiles and rockets experts, Anatoly A. Blagonravov, who is also head of the Soviet Academy's department of technical science, stated that Russian scientists will be working on Sputniks usable for radio communications on earth as one of the most important aspects of their work during the next 20 years.[8] He emphasized the need to learn how to use new radiowave bands, and, in particular, the shortest waves, as one of the key problems of radio electronics. Of interest in this regard are the principles for making use of the properties of plasmas for generating, amplifying, and transforming these bands. He indicated that it would be necessary, too, for scientists in the field of radio electronics to devise instruments on the basis of using intermolecular and interatomic fluctuations.

A few weeks earlier the U.S.S.R. Deputy Minister of Communications Konstantin Sergeychuk reported . . . in an article in the *Economic Gazette* (*Economitcheskaya Gazyeta*). . . . that "serious attention" ought to be given to the possible use of artificial earth satellites for telecasting.

He outlined communications problems of the immediate future and said that Sputniks should have sufficiently powerful relay stations to enable them to function for a number of years and with the capability of beaming all radiations from the stations toward a particular area. Telecasts could then be extended practically to unlimited areas.

Sergeychuk went on to state his belief that, because of the multinational composition of the Soviet Union, it would be necessary to transmit the sound waves of a telecast simultaneously in several languages. He forecasts a great future for color television in the U.S.S.R. and stresses that, with the introduction of broadband highly efficient communication systems in the U.S.S.R., it will be possible to develop a single, nationwide television network with regular program-exchange arrangements not only among Soviet but also with foreign television centers.

He reported that today the U.S.S.R. has some 6 million TV sets, more than 100 powerful television stations, and 200 relay centers. When the 7-year plan is accomplished there will be more than 160 television centers and several hundred relay stations in operation with the number of sets growing approximately to 15 million.

The Deputy Minister recalled that the draft program of the Communist Party of the Soviet Union ranks communications development among the decisive spheres of technical progress.

Analyzing Sergeychuk's ideas, the *London Soviet Weekly* (published by the London Soviet Embassy) reported [on September 28, 1961]:

> The U.S.S.R. is paying serious attention to the possibility of using Sputniks as TV and radio relay stations.

And finally, at the end of 1961, it has been reported that *Pravda* carried a report by Professor K. Sergeyev, prophesying the early development of a communication satellite system:

> We can anticipate shortly the creation of a system of satellite stations for purposes of communication and relaying of radio and television broadcasts, for the navigation of ships and aircraft and for systematic weather observations, Prof. K. Sergeyev says in the December 31, [1961] *Pravda*. . . .

Finally, Professor Sergeyev says, the problem of super-high-speed postal communications and cargo and passenger conveyance in rocket spaceships will probably be solved in practice.

In the Communist daily press and Soviet scientific technical journals there is a voluminous number of articles indicating Soviet scientific interest in communication from satellites to earth. In comparison there is a general paucity of information either from scientists or administrators written about a communication satellite system [such as Telstar] launched from earth to be used for relaying information.*

One may conclude after examining the Russian statements that their scientists were engaged in debates quite similar to those that took place in the United States. That the so-called synchronous satellite, that is, the satellite in 24-hour orbit, offers a great number of advantages must have been evident to the Russian scientists too. But it is equally evident that one had to wait for a number of other developments before the problem of the synchronous satellite can be solved. One, which applied to the United States more than to the Russians, was the need of very large boosters, because a great weight has to be lifted to a distant orbit. One of the first things discussed when the Saturn booster was in its final planning stage was that, of all the rockets in the Western world, only the Saturn could bring a synchronous satellite to its destination.

High payload-carrying capacity, which the Russians had before we did, is not the whole story. Synchronous satellites will have to be heavy because they need a great deal of electrical power. They are also likely to be complicated; and one has to assume, to be on the safe side, that they will need periodic

* *Communication Satellites: Technical, Economic, and International Development;* Staff Report, prepared for the use of the Committee on Aeronautical and Space Sciences, United States Senate (87th Congress, 2d Session), February 25, 1962, pp. 133–138.

maintainance, which implies the existence of manned ships for this purpose.

Therefore, both sides will have to wait for superheavy boosters, for advances in power generation in space, and for manned ships to be used for maintenance. The Russians, thinking about reliable sources for a great deal of electric power in a satellite, may easily have had another thought in mind: namely, a communication satellite broadcasting with enough power so that it can be received directly by home radio and television sets. Such a satellite is *not* an item of the immediate future, it is certainly farther from the present than the synchronous satellite. But some problems of the two systems, such as a long-lasting power supply, are similar to each other and the Russian scientists are undoubtedly aware of this similarity.

The launching of *Telstar* has, conceivably, caused a shift in the Russian plans. A well-functioning low orbit communication satellite is now no longer a novelty, and this fact may have caused existing Russian plans to be dropped unless they are so far advanced that a similar satellite can be put into orbit almost immediately. It is likely, however, that the Russians will now concentrate on the first synchronous communications satellite.

REFERENCES

1. *Review of Space Program,* Hearing Before the Committee on Science and Astronautics, U.S. House of Representatives, Jan. 20, 1960, pt. 1, p. 132.

2. *Proposed Studies on the Implications of Peaceful Space Activities for Human Affairs,* prepared for the National Aeronautics and Space Administration by the Brookings Institution (87th Congress, 1st Session, House of Representatives, Report No. 242), April 18, 1961.

3. Andrew G. Haley, "Progress Made in the Use of Radio for Protection of Life and Property in Outer Space," presented at the American Rocket Society's 15th Annual Meeting, Shoreham Hotel, Washington, D.C., December 5–8, 1960, pp. 14–15.

4. Edward C. Welsh, "Welsh Analyzes U.S. Space Expenditures," *Aviation Week,* October 30, 1961.

5. Albert Parry, *Russia's Rockets and Missiles,* Garden City, N. Y.: Doubleday & Co., Inc., 1960, pp. 208–209.

6. *Ibid.,* pp. 244–245.

7. *Space Satellite Communications, Review of the Report of the Ad Hoc Carrier Committee,* pt. 2, p. 755, November 8, 1961. Memorandum prepared by Herschel F. Clesner, assistant counsel, Subcommittee on Patents, Trade Marks, and Copyrights, Senate Judiciary Committee.

8. Report to general meeting of U.S.S.R. Academy of Science, Department of Technical Sciences, *circa* November 24, 1961.

6 Satellites for Astronomical Research

ON MARCH 7, 1962, a Thor-Delta rocket rose from Cape Canaveral to put a satellite—the first in a series—into orbit. This object bore the strange nickname of "streetcar"; the reason for this designation being the satellite's structure, which is boxlike and can be compartmented if desired. This satellite is designed to carry different scientific instruments for different flights, just as a streetcar can accommodate different passengers on different runs.

The satellite consists of a metal box, shaped like a 9-cornered polygon, about 1 foot high and 44 inches in diameter, the largest diameter the Delta rocket can accommodate. On top of this box there is a vertical semicircular "sail" carrying silicon cells that convert sunlight into electric current. The over-all height of the whole satellite is 37 inches. The sail is attached to a plate that can rotate; while the polygonal body of the satellite spins like a gyroscope to provide stabilization, the plate and the sail on top of it are driven by a synchronous motor at the rate of the spin, but in the opposite direction. The sail thereby maintains its position facing the sun.

The first of the streetcar satellites carried 13 different scientific instruments and became known as OSO, from Orbiting Solar Observatory. Its objective was to measure the different types of radiation from the sun, and it was the first astronomical satellite.

Astronomy shares with meteorology the distinction of having always been an international science. Observatories in different countries not only share information freely through publications and interobservatory memoranda called "announcement cards"; or they depend on each other for checking discoveries. An observatory in one part of the earth might continue an observation begun by another far away, knowing that dawn would stop the astronomers in the observatory that began the work. In the same way, observatories in the Northern Hemisphere can

Model of a "streetcar" type orbiting solar observatory.

rely on colleagues in the Southern Hemisphere to check on an object too close to the horizon for the northern observers. Astronomy and meteorology differ, however, as regards the urgency of communication. In the first place, astronomical events can be calculated in advance so that one can prepare for them in ample time, strongly hoping that the weather will cooperate too, when the time comes. In the second place, astronomical phenomena, with only a few specific exceptions, such as transits (the passage of Mercury or Venus across the disk of the sun) and occulations (periods when a planet or star is covered by the disk of the moon), usually last for some time. Hence astronomical work has always been characterized by a certain serenity and, in keeping with the subject matter, has lacked the frantic pace meteorologists must adopt.

But, again, both meteorology and astronomy are alike in that the advent of astronautics not only enlarges and enhances their activities; for both it means a new epoch. With the aid of artificial satellites meteorologists can see the earth as a whole, and with the aid of artificial satellites astronomers at long last can overcome the worst obstacle nature has placed in their way: our own atmosphere. The lay person, impressed by the amount of information astronomers have gathered, literally has no idea how much astronomers might know by now if they did not have to work through an atmosphere like ours.

ᛗ The Trouble with the Atmosphere

Atmospheric turbulence, air currents, and eddies make the images of the celestial bodies shimmer and dance about on the photographic plates of telescopes, so that we [anyone looking through a telescope] can only see a blur where we should see a sharp picture. The biggest telescopes on the earth normally operate with an effective resolution that is about $1/20$ of the theoretically obtainable value.

Low-energy radio waves are reflected and absorbed by the electrons and ions of the ionosphere, and never get through the atmosphere. In fact, most of the radio-frequency energy that envelops the earth cannot penetrate the ionosphere.

The earth's atmosphere is completely opaque also to wavelengths shorter than a few millimeters, and it does not "open up" until one reaches the near infrared, where ordinary light and heat rays exist. At still shorter wavelengths, because of the influence of ozone and other atmospheric gases, the earth's atmosphere blots out the ultraviolet radiation from the sun and the other stars. The so-called soft X rays emitted by the sun can only penetrate the outermost layers of the earth's atmosphere. The atmosphere in general is opaque to X rays and to gamma rays. Only the most energetic cosmic rays succeed in penetrating the earth's atmosphere down to the ground, so that information about the lower-energy primary cosmic rays is not available on the surface of the earth. Moreover, the earth's magnetic field repels low-energy primary cosmic rays and is another factor in keeping them from reaching the ground.

In fact, the plight of the earthbound observer until now may be likened to that of a man imprisoned in a stone igloo with walls and roof 10 feet thick. At the time of his imprisonment, a small hole in the roof directly overhead was his only connection with the outside world. Since then, through a great deal of labor, aided by ingenuity, he has been able to enlarge this roof opening slightly, and also to bore two small holes in the wall close to the ground, on opposite sides of his prison. Through these 3 "windows" come all the information that he is able to obtain about the world around him, and it is with this meager knowledge, coupled with his imagination, that he must construct a picture of the outside world.*

* *Space Handbook: Astronautics and Its Applications;* Staff Report of the Select Committee on Astronautics and Space Exploration, 1959, p. 211.

The "small hole in the roof" in this amusing description is the visible light; physicists and astronomers have succeeded in enlarging it a little by the use of spectroscopy and, especially, the photographic plate, which can be made sensitive to ultraviolet and infrared that the eye can no longer see under normal conditions. The "two small holes in the wall" are the information about the universe received by radio telescopes on the one hand and by cosmic-ray investigation on the other.

This discussion alone shows how much astronomy has to gain from instruments outside the atmosphere, and any astronomer has a mental list of items he would wish to investigate first, if given the chance.

₪ Artificial Satellite OSO
Investigates the Sun

Our sun is the star nearest to us—its distance from the earth early in January of every year is 91½ million miles; early in July, when the earth is at apogee, it is 94½ million miles. Astronomically speaking, the sun is a medium-small star, even though its mass is about 300,000 times that of the earth. The sun's diameter is around 860,000 miles and its surface temperature is approximately 11,000° Fahrenheit. The energy our sun pours into space in the form of light and heat is quite constant; it does not seem to vary from the average value by more than 0.5 per cent. But the sun's energy production is quite variable as regards ultraviolet radiation and radio waves. And at intervals that appear to be completely random the sun suddenly produces an intense outburst of charged subatomic particles (cosmic rays). One such outburst took place on February 23, 1956, and lasted about 18 hours. During that time the intensity of ionizing radiation above the atmosphere probably was 1,000 times the normal value. It is interesting to note, at this point, that such a fantastic outburst, prior to the invention of radio, simply went unnoticed.

The OSO satellite carried several types of detectors for X rays and atomic particles emitted by the sun, as well as a dust-particle detector. The stabilizing equipment worked excellently; its accuracy was compared to sighting a 1-cent piece from a distance of ½ mile. The satellite was in a nearly circular orbit 350 miles from sea level and needed 96.15 minutes to complete one orbit. During this time the information gathered by the instrument was stored on tape and when the satellite passed over ground stations it was ordered to transmit the information. It did so by "playing" 90 minutes of observation during the 5 minutes it was within range of the tracking station; the playback, then, was speeded up 18 times. On May 22, after 77 days in space, during which it orbited the earth 1,138 times, the satellite stopped sending useful information. Something went wrong with the spin control; the servo system, trying to keep the "sail" of solar cells in the direction of the sun, used up all the electric current available so that nothing was left for data transmission.

Surprisingly, information was received again on June 24. From the way this new material came through, NASA's scientists could determine what had probably happened. At first the spin control had become defective, instructing the gas jets by which the satellite spins to increase the rate of spin, which was not necessary. But the gas jets, obeying orders, did increase the rate from 30 revolutions per minute to 50 revolutions per minute. To equalize this high spin rate, the servo systems drained the batteries. One month later the rate of spin had slowed down to 42 revolutions per minute, either because of friction in the bearing, or else under the influence of the earth's magnetic field. The transmitter began working again, but the tape recorders did not. What was received after June 24 was direct transmission of data as the instruments gathered the information. This meant that only 19 minutes of each orbit were useful; the rest of the time the satellite was below the horizon for the tracking stations.

But during this period everything had worked properly; the first astronomical satellite had observed more than 75 solar flares and gathered much information about gamma rays and X rays from the sun. The experiment will be repeated, of course, and more astronomical satellites are planned; they are OAO (Orbiting Astronomical Observatory), to be the first astronomical telescope in orbit; EGO (Eccentric Geophysical Observ-atory, so called because it is supposed to go into a very elon-gated orbit, with its apogee at least 70,000 miles away but with a perigee of only 175–200 miles); and POGO (Polar Orbiting Geophysical Observatory), which will assume a more circular orbit, but one going over the poles of the earth.

While it is impossible for a navigational satellite to con-tribute to cloud-cover observations, almost any artificial satel-lite might contribute to astronomical knowledge. When Ex-plorer I discovered the zone of radiation around the earth called the Van Allen belt, named after Dr. James Van Allen, it was a contribution to astronomy. The Russian rocket fired for impact on the moon in September 1959 disclosed that our moon had a very weak magnetic field and therefore cannot have a Van Allen belt, and another contribution was made. When the changes in the orbit of the tiny Vanguard I satellite led to a more precise determination of the earth's shape, it was yet another astronomical discovery. Further, the Russian rocket that went into a long orbit looping behind the moon, producing a number of photographs of the far side of our natural satellite, probably has to be considered an astronomical satellite.

ℳ Information Probes and Satellites Will Furnish

The number of astronomical problems that can be solved by astronautical activities is quite large. But it is necessary at this point to establish the difference between the two space devices for astronomical research—namely, astronomical satellites and "probes." An astronomical satellite is, actually, still an earth-bound observatory differing from regular observatories mainly by its location—above the atmosphere—and by the fact that it is, at present, still unmanned. The function of an astronomical satellite is still observation from a distance. A probe, on the other hand, is a device that actually travels to the body to be observed, accomplishing actual contact or at least a close course.

Let us look at the problems that can be solved using these devices. Beginning at the center of the solar system, the first set of problems concerns:

The sun. At the moment, the main questions are still about the nature of sunspots and the so-called solar flares that are associated with sunspots and that often, but apparently not always, produce outbursts of atomic particles. The periodicity of the sunspots is also unexplained. All these problems seem to require continued observations over long periods of time for their solution. Much can be done in this direction with satellites like OSO, but there is the additional possibilty of producing a solar satellite having the same relationship to the sun as the 24-hour-orbit satellite has to the earth. The sun turns on its axis once in 25 days, so the projected solar satellite would have to have a 25-day orbit around the sun. Such an orbit is difficult to accomplish, but once a solar satellite is in operation, the results should be definitive.

Mercury. The planet closest to the sun, Mercury, is difficult to observe because of its proximity to that body; hence, our knowledge of its physical characteristics is less accurate than for some of the other members of the solar system. Mercury has no moon, and its mass is not known with precision, but is of the order of $\frac{1}{20}$ that of the earth. This much is known, however: It is a small rocky sphere, about $\frac{1}{2}$ again as large as the earth's moon, and it always keeps the same side turned toward the sun. The sunlit half is thus extremely hot, probably having maximum surface temperatures as high as 750°F., while the side in perpetual darkness is extremely cold, cold enough to retain frozen gases, with temperatures approaching absolute zero. Mercury is not known to have any atmosphere, nor would a permanent gaseous envelope be expected to occur under the conditions existing on the planet. Its rocky surface is probably somewhat similar to that of our moon.

Venus. Even less is known with confidence about the surface conditions on Venus. Therefore, many statements about it are necessarily more speculative than definitive. In dimensions and mass it is slightly smaller than the earth, but no astronomer has ever seen its solid surface, since its dense and turbulent atmosphere, containing white particles in suspension, is opaque to light of all wave lengths. Some water vapor has been detected on Venus, but carbon dioxide is abundant in its atmosphere, as determined by spectrographic analysis of the light reflected from the upper reaches of its visible cloud deck. On the basis of all the available evidence, it may be presumed that the surface of Venus is probably hot, dry, dusty, windy, and dark beneath a continuous dust storm; that the atmospheric pressure is probably several times the normal barometric pressure at the surface of the earth; and that carbon dioxide is probably the major atmospheric gas, with nitrogen and argon also present as minor constituents.

Mars. Much more complete information is available about Mars, but many questions about surface conditions still remain unanswered. With a diameter halfway between that of the moon and the earth, and a rate of revolution and inclination of equator to orbital plane closely similar to those of the earth, it has an appreciable atmosphere and its surface markings exhibit seasonal changes in coloration. Its white polar caps, appearing in winter and vanishing in summer, are apparently thin layers of frozen water (frost) of the order of fractions of an inch to several inches in thickness. The atmospheric pressure at the surface has been estimated at 8 to 12 per cent of the earth sea-level normal, and the atmosphere is believed to consist largely of nitrogen. No free oxygen has been detected in its atmosphere. Topographically, its surface is quite flat with no very abrupt changes in elevation and no prominent mountains. The "climate" would be similar to that of a high desert on the earth to an exaggerated degree (about 11 miles high, in fact) with noon summer temperatures in the tropics reaching a maximum of perhaps 80° to 90°F., but falling rapidly during the evening to reach a minimum before dawn of the order of −100°F. The interval between 2 successive close approaches of the earth and Mars is slightly over 2 years. At opposition, that is, when the 2 planets lie in the same direction from the sun, the approximate distance between the earth and Mars ranges from 35 million to 60 million miles.

Bleak and desert-like as Mars appears to be, with no free oxygen and little, if any, water, there is rather good evidence that some indigenous life forms may exist.

The seasonal color changes, from green in spring to brown in autumn, suggests vegetation. Recently Sinton [William M. Sinton of Lowell Observatory in *Science*, 1959, p. 1234] has found spectroscopic evidence that organic molecules may be responsible for the Martian dark areas. The objections raised concerning differences between the color and infrared reflectivities of terrestrial organic matter and those of the dark areas on Mars have been successfully met by the excellent work of Professor G. A. Tikhov and his colleagues of the new Soviet Institute of Astrobiology. Tikhov has shown that Arctic plants differ in infrared reflection from temperate and tropical plants, and an extrapolation to Martian conditions leads to the conclusion that the dark areas are really Martian vegetable life.

Although human life could not survive without extensive local environmental modifications, the possibility of a self-sustaining colony is not ruled out.

The giant planets. The four members of this group of planets (Jupiter, Saturn, Uranus, Neptune) have so many characteristics in common that they may well be treated together. They are all massive bodies of low density and large diameter. They all rotate rapidly. Because of their low densities (0.7 to 1.6 times the density of water), and on the basis of spectral information, they all are thought to have a "rock-in-a-snowball" structure; that is, a small dense rocky core surrounded by a thick shell of ice and covered by thousands of miles of compressed hydrogen and helium. Methane and ammonia are also known to be present as minor constituents. Because of the low intensities of solar radiation at the distances of the giant planets, temperatures at the visible upper atmospheric surfaces range from −200°F. to −300°F. A number of the satellites of Jupiter, Saturn, and Neptune are larger than the earth's moon, and some may be as large as Mercury. Although reliable physical data on these satellites are lacking, it is possible that they might be somewhat more hospitable for space flight missions than the planets about which they orbit.

Pluto. Almost nothing is known about this extreme member of the known solar system except its orbital characteristics and the fact that it is extremely cold, with a small radius and a mass about 80 per cent that of the earth.[*]

[*] From *Space Handbook: Astronautics and its Application, op. cit.,* pp. 12–13.

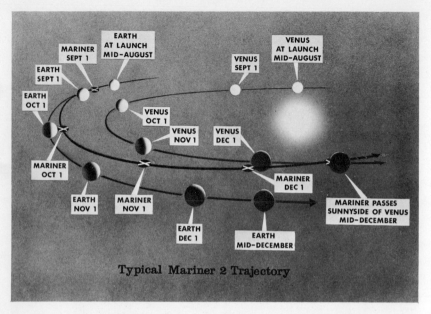

Path of Mariner II, the Venus planetary probe.

For some time to come, additions to our knowledge about Mercury will have to come from astronomical satellites orbiting the earth, but the problems posed by cloud-veiled Venus are being attacked by means of "close fly-bys" by planetary probes. On August 27, 1962, one of these probes, named Mariner II, was launched successfully from Cape Canaveral and is expected to pass within 9,000 miles of Venus early in December. Mars, too, is in quite easy reach of a planetary probe, but Jupiter and the planets beyond it are too far away to be reached by probes in the near future.

As regards our own moon, it was omitted from this list of astronomical problems because it is so near. This nearness does not mean that no questions remain to be answered, but NASA's program of lunar exploration by fly-by probes, probes to orbit around the moon, probes to land instrument packages, and, finally, manned landing craft is such that the exploration of the

Model of a Mariner probe on its flight past Venus. The probe is expected to make infrared and microwave measurements of the planet.

A Mariner probe undergoing a check before the solar panels are attached.

moon begins to lose its astronomical character. Astronomical observation always implies looking at the object under study from a distance without the possibility of physical contact, and NASA's program for the moon has therefore more the aspect of an exploration of a distant continent that is difficult to reach.

In reference to the discoveries that astronomical satellites are likely to make in the field of stellar astronomy, the long-distance exploration of the other stars in space, it can only be repeated that a new era of scientific research and theory is about to begin.

7 Man in Orbit

It is not within the scope of this book to deal with manned spaceships and interplanetary travel. Such journeys are in the main still theoretical and not yet practical, but the space theory that has, of course, by now become a fact is sending a man into space. Testing man's endurance and performance during rocket take off, in orbit, and during return, constitute another significant aspect of our research in space. In fact, as has been stated in the Introduction, the Age of Space began with thoughts about manned flight. Ziolkovsky and Ganswindt, Oberth and Hohmann, all the early thinkers about space travel—with the sole exception of Dr. Robert H. Goddard—thought that space would be explored by manned ships.

The exploration of space began, however, by means of unmanned satellites. The reason was two-fold; in the first place, nobody was willing to sacrifice a man in an endeavor where so many unknown factors were involved. Another and very weighty reason was that no rocket available in 1957 and 1958 could have lifted the weight of a capsule capable of holding a man and keeping him alive. Because unmanned satellites made a number of discoveries, many people (the group was not restricted to any particular profession or habit of thought since it included administrators and engineers, mathematicians and politicians, physicists and sociologists) began to wonder whether many goals could not be accomplished by unmanned devices and whether there was any need for manned flight. Dr.

Vannevar Bush, now chairman of the Board of Governors at M.I.T., even went so far as to label plans for manned orbits a "stunt" (the *New York Times,* April 7, 1960), while Richard van de Riet Wooley, the Astronomer Royal of England, referred to manned space travel as "balderdash" (as was also stated in the *New York Times,* about 5 years ago).

By 1959 the Russians had stated that they were looking forward to manned orbits, though they did not give any anticipated dates. The United States announced a program for manned orbits named Project Mercury. Its purpose and some of the details were admirably explained in a speech by George M. Low, Chief of Manned Space Flight at NASA headquarters. The speech, to the United Press International Editors Conference in Washington D.C. was delivered on September 9, 1960 (that is before anybody, Russian or American, had attained orbit), and although it is now somewhat out of date in that it refers to manned orbits as something still to be accomplished it deserves to be quoted.*

Ⓜ Project Mercury

It has been suggested that I give you a progress report on Project Mercury, and devote some time to the seven astronauts, to their training program, and to the human aspects of the program in general.

I will try to comply with this request, but before I do I would like to dispel some common misconceptions about Project Mercury. What are these misconceptions? Let me list them for you. First, it has been stated that Project Mercury is merely a stunt, a stunt that has no technical merit and leads only to a dead end. Secondly, it has been said that Project Mercury is designed only to win an important first in the space program, to fly a manned satellite before the Soviets do, and, third, it has been said that Project Mercury should be terminated if the Soviets achieve

* From a transcript of the tape recording.

manned orbital flight before we do. I would like to discuss these misconceptions one by one.

First, is Project Mercury a stunt? Let me assure you that it is not. Rather, it is an important and necessary step in our over-all program for the manned exploration of space. It should not be necessary to point out to this audience that man is destined to play a vital and direct role in the exploration of the moon and of the planets. In this regard, it is not easy to conceive that instruments could be devised that can effectively and reliably duplicate man's role as an explorer, a geologist, a surveyor, a photographer, a chemist, a biologist, or a host of other specialists whose talents would be needed. In all of these areas man's judgment, his ability to observe and to reason, and his decision-making capabilities are required. Only man can cope with the unexpected, and the unexpected of course, is the most interesting.

Project Mercury is but the initial step in a long-range program for the manned exploration of space. It will lead to the development of an advanced manned spacecraft, a spacecraft that will have the capabilities both of manned circumlunar flight and of serving useful functions as an earth-orbiting laboratory. We have called the spacecraft the Apollo spacecraft. . . . Project Apollo will lead to manned landings on the moon and on the planets, and to the establishment of a permanent, manned space station.

Before we can proceed with Project Apollo, we must know how man will react in a space environment, what his capabilities will be, and what must be provided in a spacecraft to allow a man to function usefully. This is where Project Mercury comes into the picture. From Mercury we expect to learn the answers to these and many other questions, but the determination of man's capabilities in the space environment is only one of the benefits that is being gained from Project Mercury. Of equal importance is the technical knowledge being gained during the design, engineering, and operation of the first vehicle specifically engineered for man's flight in space. Let us repeat, then, Project Mercury is by no means a stunt. Rather, it is a necessary step in any program leading toward manned exploration into space.

Next, let me take up the second point. This is the question concerning the urgency of Project Mercury. Does this urgency stem only from a desire to beat the Russians? Again, the answer must be no. If the only justification for this project were to establish an important first, then it is quite clear that we never should have initiated the program, for it is well known that the Soviets took the first step in a manned space-flight program long before 1957. In November 1957, they orbited the dog, Laika, an obvious indication of the general direction of their space effort. Certainly, it is clear that if they were able to achieve Sputnik II in November 1957 and have an animal alive in the satellite for a number of days, they must have started this program two, or perhaps more years, before 1957. The National Aeronautics and Space Administration was not established until October 1958. This was nearly a year after it was evident that the Russians were well under way in a manned space-flight program and perhaps 3 to 4 years after they had initiated their program.

Project Mercury was then initiated by us with a clear understanding that the Russians would most likely achieve

manned orbital flight before we would, and this understanding was recently confirmed by the Soviet achievement in connection with Sputniks IV and V. Sputnik IV,
as you will recall, was a 10,000-pound spaceship that by
their admission had a capability of supporting man in a
space environment. This spaceship was launched in May of
this year [1960], and more recently—just last August—this
same spaceship was launched with a payload of two dogs
and was successfully recovered one day later. Based on the
available information on Sputniks IV and V, I am firmly
convinced that the Soviets now have the capability of
achieving manned orbital flight. They themselves have
stated that it is an important goal in their space program,
and I believe they are now waiting only for the appropriate
time before they will send the first man, or perhaps men,
into space.

You might ask then, why are we pursuing Project Mercury with utmost urgency? The answer to this question is
relatively simple, even though we are not in a race with
Project Mercury, and if this were a race I believe we would
have lost it before we crossed the starting line. I believe
this nation should attempt real leadership in the space program in the future. In the area of manned space flight, such
leadership could be realized through the vigorous implementation of Project Apollo. But, as I mentioned earlier,
before Apollo can go very far downstream, we must learn
much about man's capabilities in space and about the general technology of manned space flight. This is basically
why it is most important to do Project Mercury, and to do
it soon.

Now, for my third point. Should Project Mercury be terminated when the Soviets achieve manned orbital flight? The answer to this question should be quite obvious from my preceding discussion, because Project Mercury is an important step leading toward Project Apollo. It must be carried out regardless of Russian achievement. Perhaps the true nature of this third question can be shown by an analogy. Should we have stopped at the development of jet airliners just because the British and the Russians developed jet aircraft before we did? Clearly we should not have, and we did not stop after this development. As a result, the United States is now an undisputed leader in the jet transport field. Similarly, a continuing effort on Project Mercury may lead to eventual leadership by the United States in the manned exploration of space, while the termination of this project would most certainly keep us in second place.

I might add one other point here. If there were complete cooperation between nations in the space program, or perhaps in all other programs, then my last point would not be valid. If the Soviets would tell us, and we would exchange with them, all information that is available on the technology acquired to do a project like Mercury or Sputnik or Apollo—if they would give us all their information and we would give them all of ours—then we might skip some of the steps in our program. This is an area where international cooperation could, I believe, help both of our countries.

Now I would like to describe briefly what is involved in Project Mercury. The Mercury mission proposes to launch from Cape Canaveral a satellite capsule using an Atlas launch vehicle. On top of the capsule there is a tower-like structure. The tower is an escape system that would be activated in case the launch vehicle malfunctioned during the early stages of flight. In a normal mission this escape tower is jettisoned about the time the Atlas leaves the earth's atmosphere, and the Atlas sustainer carries the satellite into orbit. Once in orbit the satellite is separated from the Atlas through the use of small separation rockets, and the capsule is then turned around to orbit the earth at an altitude of more than 100 miles for probably 3 orbits.

At the completion of the third orbit around the earth the capsule's retrorockets, small solid-propellant rockets located on the blunt end of the capsule, would be fired. The retrorockets reduce the speed of the satellite by about 350 miles per hour. In orbit the satellite will travel about 17,500 miles per hour, and slowing it down by only 350 miles per hour is sufficient to allow the earth's gravity to reassert itself and pull the satellite slowly back down toward the atmosphere. The satellite will then fly toward the atmosphere, re-enter the atmosphere, and be slowed down by the drag of the earth from its very high satellite velocity to a speed of perhaps 600 miles per hour. During this time the front end of the capsule will glow with the heat of friction, and the astronaut will be thrust back into his supporting couch with 8 times the force of gravity (8 Gs). Then at an altitude of about 42,000 feet, a small parachute is deployed to stabilize the capsule, and still later, at an altitude of 10,000 feet, a large cargo-type parachute is deployed to lower the capsule rather gently to the Atlantic Ocean. There it will be picked up by ships that are standing by. . . .

⚏ The Capsule

The cone-shaped capsule is about 6 feet in diameter and 9 feet along its vertical dimension. Within this pressure-type capsule, the astronaut is supported in an individually form-fitted couch, designed so that he can take the high

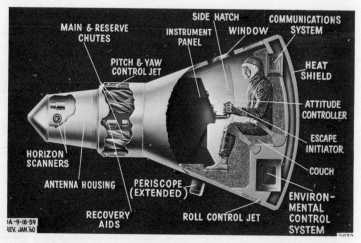

Drawing of Project Mercury's capsule showing instruments and control equipment.

forces that are entailed in a launching and again during the deceleration and re-entry into the atmosphere. The atmosphere within the cabin will be controlled by an environmental control system. The communication system will be used for communications with the tracking and telemetry stations. In orbit the capsule's attitude will be

Mercury capsule undergoing weight-and-balance tests at Cape Canaveral.

maintained. It will be sent through some infrared horizon scanners that will establish a horizontal plane to which the attitude can be referenced. Small reaction control jets automatically stabilize the capsule in a prescribed attitude in orbit. In addition to these automatic devices the pilot himself can also maintain the cabin's atmosphere and the capsule's attitude. He has an instrument-panel periscope by which he can see the ground in order to reference the capsule to the proper attitude. He also has a manual attitude controller by which he can control these small jets and thereby stabilize the capsule in case the automatic system should fail.

The shape of the capsule itself was determined primarily for consideration of the capsule entry into the atmosphere. At the blunt end is an ablation heat shield that will dissipate the tremendous heat of re-entry. At the small end are held the parachutes used in the final stages of descent and the antennas for the various communication systems.

By looking at a picture of the capsule you might think that it is a relatively simple device, but such is by no means the case. In the first place, the capsule has to be relatively light, weighing little more than a ton; it has to be this light so that our Atlas booster can boost it into satellite orbit. It has been a major engineering task to design a capsule that is small enough to do the mission, light enough to do the mission, and yet has reliable subsystems to accomplish the mission safely. Each of the various systems in the capsule, the environmental system, the communication systems, the attitude-control systems, and so forth, had to be especially designed for this Mercury vehicle. Perhaps I can best illustrate how complicated the device is by stating that there are 7 miles of electrical wiring interwoven into the capsule to allow to accomplish its difficult mission. These wires are needed to interconnect the power supplies, the various electronic gear, communications gear, the squib rockets, lights, and everything else in the capsule. I mentioned earlier that NASA was formed in October 1958. Shortly thereafter we initiated procedures to contract for the Mercury capsule. In January of 1959 we selected Mc-Donnell Aircraft Corporation, on the basis of a competitive bid, as the contractor to build these capsules. We have ordered at this time 24 Mercury capsules, the first one of which was delivered in April 1960, about 14 months after the order was placed with McDonnell. To date [September 1960], 4 additional capsules have been delivered, totaling 5 capsules that have been delivered in a period of less than 2 years since the program was started. This was accomplished primarily by first of all doing the design, engineering, and manufacturing almost simultaneously. Secondly, the effort by the people directly engaged in this program has always been a very concentrated one. At McDonnell, for example, people are working now on a 3-shift, 7-day-a-week basis to get the capsules out as quickly as possible.

The first capsule delivered in April of 1960 was flown in May of this year in a so-called beach abort test where we simulated the escape maneuver by launching the capsule with only its escape tower. This test was quite successful.

A very important flight of the Mercury capsule was planned for July 29 of this year. This was to be the first test of a production Mercury capsule using the Atlas booster. Now I might mention that before this test we had once before flown a Mercury-type capsule using an Atlas—the so-called "Big Joe" flight of September 9, 1959—but in this test we used a so-called "boiler plate" capsule—a capsule that duplicated the shape and size of the Mercury capsule but very much heavier than the actual production capsule. On July 29 of this year we were going to have our first severe test of the capsule qualification of the Mercury capsule under severe re-entry conditions in a 1,500-mile ballistic flight using the Atlas booster. The capsule was to have achieved a velocity of 19,000 feet per second, reach an altitude of 110 miles and a maximum deceleration during re-entry of 16½ Gs. Unfortunately this test failed, due to a malfunction of the Atlas booster. About 1 minute after launch the Atlas failed catastrophically. The capsule was thrown clear of the Atlas, but of course none of the mission objectives was accomplished. The capsule, incidentally, remained intact until water impact and has been examined subsequently to gain some test data. But, as I mentioned before, the basic objectives of the test were not achieved. We plan to repeat this test in a continuing program building up toward the manned orbital flights.

Another facet of the Mercury program is the series of the Redstone ballistic flights to test and qualify the capsule under some less severe conditions. In these flights the capsule will be boosted to an altitude of 125 miles, down range 200 miles, and it will sustain a period of about 5½ minutes of weightlessness. These tests will be conducted first with only instrumented capsules, later on with a capsule containing a chimpanzee, and finally, after we are convinced that all the systems are sufficiently reliable, we plan to make manned ballistic flights using the Redstone launch vehicle. In these flights the man will be subjected to more than 5 times the amount of weightlessness than we are able to do in aircraft-type tests, and he will sustain the high accelerations of launch and the high decelerations of re-entry. We believe then that these tests will be an important part in the training program of the astronauts before they can undertake orbital missions. After all of these ballistic flights, both of the Redstone and the Atlas, the orbital flights using the Atlas will take place.

ⓦ Work of the Astronauts

Now, to get to the discussion of where the astronaut fits into this program and what his functions are. By examining the instrument panel of the capsule one can see that the pilot's role will be a fairly active one in the Mercury mission. There are series of lights that will go on, red or green, depending on whether a certain function is performed automatically at the proper time or if it is not. For example, if the retrorockets do not fire at the proper time— this of course is the important event that is needed to get the capsule back down—he gets a red light on the panel and he himself then could, by mechanical means, as opposed to an electrical circuit, take action and fire the retrorockets in order to get the capsule down in case the automatic system should fail. There are also mechanical controls for the life-support, air-conditioning, communications, and attitude-control systems, should these automatic devices fail.

I do not think I have to go into the history of who the astronauts are or how they were selected, for this has been

Project Mercury astronauts, left to right: Walter Schirra, Donald Slayton, Virgil Grissom, Christopher C. Craft of Mercury Operations Division, astronauts Gordon Cooper, Scott Carpenter, John Glenn, and Alan Shepard.

well publicized. I would like briefly to discuss what they have been doing, what their training program is, and why we are going through this. I think the question is answered for the most part in discussion of the instrument panel. In order to take care of all possible normal and emergency conditions, the man must be fully qualified to perform all of these functions. He must be trained to perform on the ground as many of the things as possible before the flight testing is started. For example a very important aspect of the program is the simulation of the high-G forces, the high accelerations and decelerations, that would be encountered in flight during the launching and re-entry. This is done in the centrifuge at Johnsville, Pennsylvania. It spins about its axis simulating these high-G forces while the pilot or astronaut is in a cabin and can take proper action if the cabin's attitude, simulated attitude, would be incorrect.

We cannot simulate weightlessness on the ground but we can simulate it for periods of seconds in flights of high-performance aircraft. In a C-131 aircraft one can achieve 15 seconds of weightlessness. In supersonic airplanes we can simulate up to 1 minute of weightlessness, and, incidentally, I believe most of the astronauts prefer this state of weightlessness to the high Gs that they encounter in the centrifuge. Another facet of the training program, and I am just touching on a very few of them, is the practicing of getting out of the capsule under rough sea conditions. In practice sessions dummy Mercury capsules are placed in a tank rocked by the waves, and the astronauts climb out of the tops of the capsules.

Now let me get back to where Project Mercury fits into our long-range plans and into Project Apollo. The Apollo spacecraft will be designed for dual-mission capability. It will have the capability of manned lunar reconnaissance as a necessary and logical intermediate step before a manned landing on the moon can be achieved. In these manned circumlunar flights many, but certainly not all, of the problems will be solved that will be encountered in a manned lunar landing. Secondly, the Apollo spacecraft will be sufficiently flexible to have the capability also to serve as a manned orbiting laboratory—a laboratory where we can perform useful functions in a near-earth orbit. This orbiting laboratory is a necessary intermediate step leading toward a permanent manned space station.

Let me say a little more about this dual-mission capability, one an earth orbit, the second a circumlunar flight. In both cases the Saturn launch vehicle will be used to accomplish these missions. In order to achieve this flexibility and dual-mission capability we believe the most logical concept to pursue is a so-called modular concept of vehicle design and construction. In our present concept the Apollo spacecraft would be composed of 3 separate components or modules: the command-center module, the propulsion module, and the mission module. During launch the men would be housed in the command-center module. At least 1 of the crew members would remain in the command-center module for the entire mission to perform the complete control over the mission, and all the crew members would be back in this module for the re-entry phase of flight. Only this command center would have the capability of re-entering the earth's atmosphere. This module would probably be the same for both the earth-orbital and the circumlunar missions.

The second module would be the so-called propulsion module. This is a rather severe requirement, and early calculations have shown that this propulsion module would be as heavy or heavier perhaps than any of the other modules for the circumlunar mission. In addition to providing abort capabilities, it would also be used for maneuvering in orbit in the case of an earth-orbiting laboratory or rendezvous with satellites. It would be used for midcourse and final-course corrections for the circumlunar mission, and it could also be used to place the spacecraft into a near orbit around the moon and ejected from that orbit before it comes back to earth.

Finally, the mission modules would in all probability differ from the earth orbital and circumlunar mission. For the circumlunar mission, it would provide a minimum amount of life-support systems and instrumentation as required for lunar reconnaissance. For the earth orbital mission, because any launch vehicle, the Saturn in particular, can carry much more weight into an earth orbit than it could around the moon, this mission module could be very much larger for the earth-orbital mission than for the circumlunar mission and contain a large amount of scientific instrumentation as an orbiting laboratory.

Let me now try to sum up the current status of our manned space flight program. Project Mercury, the initial step in this program, is now nearly two years old. In this time period an extensive wind-tunnel and flight-test program has been carried out. The program involves hundreds of wind-tunnel and airplane tests and 5 major rocket flights. Also in this time period, the Mercury production capsules were designed, engineered, and tested. Five of them have been delivered to date, and we now stand at the threshold of a major flight-test program of short- and long-range ballistic flights leading first to unmanned and later on to manned orbital flights.

ᙀ The Manned Orbital Flights

The reader will have noticed that Mr. Low's speech was prophetic in several respects. The Russians did orbit a man, or rather 2, before the United States and the Mercury 3-orbit flights were performed precisely as predicted.

The method by which the Russians arrived at orbital flight was not quite the same as that of the United States. The Space Agency began with suborbital flights by animals, then orbited an instrumented Mercury capsule, followed by a chimpanzee. Meanwhile manned suborbital flights were carried out and, finally, manned orbital flights. The Russians began by orbiting a dog, then carried out numerous suborbital flights with animal capsules, and went from there directly to manned orbital flight. To the best of our knowledge they skipped the phase of manned suborbital flights.

Table 9

A LIST OF RUSSIAN AND AMERICAN MANNED ORBITAL FLIGHTS (Status of October 1, 1962)

	Name of Astronaut	Date	Apogee (MILES)	Perigee (MILES)	Number of orbits and duration
Vostok I	Gagarin	Apr. 13, 1961	187.75	109.5	1; 89.1 min.
Freedom 7	Shepard	May 5, 1961	116.5	–	1; 89.1 min.
Liberty Bell 7	Grissom	July 21, 1961	118	–	suborbital; 5 min.
Vostok II	Titov	Aug. 6, 1961	115.3	110.3	17½; 25 hrs., 18 min.
Friendship 7	Glenn	Feb. 20, 1962	160	100	3; 4 hrs., 56 min.
Aurora 7	Carpenter	May 24, 1962	167	99	3; 4 hrs., 50 min.
Vostok III	Nikolayev	Aug. 11, 1962	156	113	64; 94 hrs., 35 min.
Vostok IV	Popovich	Aug. 12, 1962	157	112	48; 70 hrs., 59 min.
Sigma 7	Schirra	Oct. 3, 1962	176	100	5¾; 9 hrs., 13 min.

The American habit of progressing by smaller and more cautious steps has resulted in the insertion of one more phase between Project Mercury and Project Apollo, namely the 2-man capsule known as Project Gemini, which will precede Apollo. It is very likely that the results of the Gemini flights will influence the design of Apollo so that nothing definite can be said at this time.

That man in orbit is not a "stunt" should be abundantly clear by now. But the very first manned orbital flight showed that

Russia's astronauts, Gherman Titov (*left*) and Yuri Gagarin.

man is even more important than had been thought. Colonel John H. Glenn, when asked by Senator Cannon, made this clear. This is the exchange that took place:

SENATOR CANNON: Colonel, you said that one of the most important things you discovered was that man can satisfactorily operate in space, and you also pointed out that this particular shot might have failed had it not been for a man aboard, because of the failure of a part of the system. As you know there has been considerable argument going on as to whether man can better perform missions in space and outer space than a machine. Would it be fair to assume, from your experience here, that we are not at a technical state today where man can satisfactorily be replaced in space or in the atmosphere for the performance of missions by machines in our present state of technological development?

COLONEL GLENN: I feel, sir, that we are already at the point where we can gain far more from the experiments we want to carry out by having a man aboard. Early in the program, we could get as much probably at one time on certain early experiments by making just an instrumented machine and sending it up and back. But we are looking forward to the time when we will have power sufficient to go out and actually stay in space for extended periods of time, make extended observations, conduct scientific experiments that will be fairly complicated. If we have power sufficient at that time, of course, we will want to maybe change course, drive around in your spacecraft as you do now in an airplane, for instance, and go where you want to go to do and see and make the observations that are best to be made. Looking forward to that time where an intelligent human being in space is mandatory, there are some things that we can never foresee doing with machines; looking forward to that time when we are not as power limited as we are now, at that time we can go out into space with a man aboard and make tremendous advancements, where, if you have to program all this in advance and send it [a machine] out on a specific mission and back, you have no flexibility at all. I think we are at the point now where we can foresee in the future power plants that will enable us to do a lot of these things.*

* From *Orbital Flight of John H. Glenn, Jr.*, Hearing before the Senate Committee on Aeronautical and Space Sciences; Testimony of Astronauts and NASA officials, held on February 28, 1962. (87th Congress, 2d Session, Senate, Document No. 79), page 23.

John H. Glenn, Jr.

Commander Shepard, the first American astronaut to make a suborbital flight, added at this point, "I think you cannot categorically say that a man should be in every space vehicle. Obviously, there are conditions where you are investigating a specific area, for example radiation belts, or you are investigating a particular communications phenomenon, as is being discussed in the committee at this time. . . . I think in these areas, machines, electronic devices, do far better than the man does."

A. Nikolayev and P. Popovich, Russia's "dual flight" astronauts.

Taken together these two statements tell the story: manned flight where it comes to explorations, which include an element of the unforeseeable; machines where a specific phenomenon is to be investigated, especially if it is in the nature of the investigation that it will take a long time, weeks, months or even years. And machines also for doing routine work, such as scanning the earth's cloud cover or repeating radio signals for communication.

8 The By-Products of Space Research

THE DICTIONARY defines a by-product as something produced apart from, or in addition to, the main product in a specific process. The production of arsenic in an iron smelter, or of ethyl alcohol in a baking oven, are typical examples.

The present plans for utilizing the space around us do not yield any direct product, comparable to the pig iron of the smelter or the loaves of bread in the baking oven. They aim at services, better weather forecasting, additional aids to navigation, better telephone service over very long distances, new discoveries that will increase our understanding of nature.

But there are by-products just the same, although they are somewhat different from the normal industrial by-product usually sold by the pound or by the ton. The by-products of space research are primarily new production and engineering methods, processes, and equipment. There are also new materials and components that have been developed to meet the needs of space research for which commercial uses have been found. These by-products have been summarized by various spokesmen of technology, and a list of them was presented by General James M. Gavin in an address to the International Bankers Association, Bal Harbor, Florida on December 2, 1958. By that time the most obvious and most useful by-products of space research had been realized.

First, there is the high-speed computer. Developed initially to meet military demands for faster calculation, the computer is an integral part of American industry, making it possible to do many operations with a high degree of efficiency and accuracy. Thermoelectric devices [which convert heat directly into electricity] for heating and cooling, now adapted for commercial applications, were originally designed to provide energy sources for space vehicles. The glass industry, as a result of work done during and after World War II on lenses and plastics, promises substantial gains in the consumer fields of optics and foods. Pyroceram [a high-strength, highly heat-resistant compound], developed for missile radomes [the top parts of missiles housing radar equipment] is now being used in the manufacture of pots and pans. Materials suitable for use in the nuclear preservation of food may make us even better fed than we already are.

Medical research, and our health problems, can use such things as film resistance thermometers. Electronic equipment capable of measuring low-level electrical signals is being adapted to measure body temperature and blood flow. In a dramatic breakthrough, illustrating unexpected benefits of research, it has been found that a derivative of hydrazine, developed as a liquid missile propellant, is useful in treating certain mental illnesses and tuberculosis.

Of course, the aeronautics industry has benefited tremendously. Engines, automatic pilots, radar systems, flight equipment capable of meeting the high standards required by space vehicles represent a great improvement over our already excellent aircraft.

A plasma arc torch (has been) developed for fabricating ultrahard materials and coatings by mass-production methods. The torch, an outgrowth of plasma [partly ionized hot gas] technology, develops heats of 30,000° and can work within tolerances of $\frac{2}{1000}$ of an inch. Another application from the missile field, which shows real possibilities, is a reliable flow meter that has no packings or bearings. This was first developed for measuring liquefied gases and should have a very wide industrial usefulness. It may even lead to improvements in marine devices for measuring distance and velocity.

Ground-to-air missiles that ride a beam to their targets must measure the distance to the target plane with an accuracy of a few feet in several miles. This principle, now being applied to surveying techniques, has revolutionized the surveying industry.

The solenoid valve, which seats itself softly enough to eliminate vibration, has been applied very satisfactorily to home-heating systems.

The use of the jet drilling for mining is another, and worthy of amplification. Missiles are already working the economically unminable taconite ore [a flintlike rock] of the Mesabi Range [of northeast Minnesota], have helped build the St. Lawrence Seaway [a waterway between Canada and the United States linking the St. Lawrence River to Lake Ontario], and are bringing down costs in quarrying.

It is estimated that taconite will be supplying about a third of our ores in less than 20 years. Until 1947 we were unable to mine this very hard rock, and then suitable rotary and churn drills were produced. Jet drilling, now available, cracks and crumble stone layers by thermally induced expansion and is somewhere between 3 and 5 times faster than rotaries.

Jet piercing can take us far deeper into the earth than we have been able to go so far, to new sources of ore and hydrocarbons.

In stone quarrying, jet spalling and channeling are proven techniques. Stone quarrying has been expensive and wasteful heretofore. Rocket flame equipment allows cutting along the natural cleavage planes, or crystal boundaries—hence it cuts stone thin without danger of cracking and, in addition, produces a fine finish that cannot be obtained when cutting by steel or abrasive tools.

Scientific literature is beginning to contain speculations on using the principle of the missile engine to save unstable intermediate products of the chemical processes. The high heats achieved in the rocket engine can, perhaps, be utilized to produce desired products that would be lost by slow cooling. But the high rate of cooling accomplished by expanding gases through the engine nozzle, it is thought, would save these unstable compounds.

Infrared [heat-ray technology] has come into its own through missile electronics. Infrared—since it cannot be jammed—appears to be challenging radar for use in guidance devices, tracking systems, and reconnaissance vehicles. Infrared is being used industrially to measure the compositions of fluids in complex processes of chemical petroleum refining and distilling. Infrared cameras are used in analyzing metallurgical material processing operations, to aid in accuracy and quality control. The entire infrared field should be significantly assisted in its growth and application through our missile-space programs. . . .

In the near future, when guidance devices permit soft landing, rocket-cargo and passenger transport will become feasible. Mail may become almost as swift as telephone.

We are making rapid progress in the economics of space travel: payload costs for Vanguard were about $1 billion a pound; for the near future launchings, payload cost should be about $1,000 per pound. When payload costs are about $100 a pound we may expect commercial space flight.

ﺏ Consumer Space-Research Goods

Hundreds of other examples of the space program's value for everyday living could be cited.

One with wide possibilities is a new welding process using a high-powered electron beam gun, developed for the fabrication of spaceships and other space vehicles. This method permits welding joints capable of withstanding temperatures up to 3,000°F.; it can be used on metals such as molybdenum and pure tungsten. And, its developers say, it results in welded joints that have deep penetration and narrow weld beads that are virtually free of contamination.

Another ingenious application, resulting from the Navy's space-research program, has significant utility for medicine and surgery. This is a glass-fiber device that, when placed in the mouth during dental work or in the area of surgical incision, permits a much magnified televising of the operation. It holds considerable promise for teaching technques in many fields.

Another example is a finely woven stainless-steel cloth designed for parachuting space vehicles back to earth. The cloth is made of fine wire of great strength that can withstand tremendous temperatures and chemical contamination. The wire from which the cloth is woven is about ⅕ the thickness of a human hair and is believed to have marked potential for industry and consumers alike.

Here is an additional list of examples:

Microminiature transmitters and receivers—used by police and doctors.

Target drone autopilot—used as an inexpensive pilot assist and safety device for private aircraft.

Inert thread-sealing compound—used by pump manufacturers serving process industries.

Satellite scan devices—used in infrared appliances, for example, lamps, roasters, switches, ovens.

Automatic control components—used as proximity switches, plugs, valves, cylinders; other components already are an integral part of industrial conveyor systems.

Missile accelerometers, torquemeters, strain gage equipment—used in auto crash tests, motor testing, shipbuilding, and bridge construction.

Space recording equipment automatically stopped and started by sound of voice—used widely as conference recorder.

Armalite radar—used as a proximity warning device for aircraft.

Miniature electronics and bearings—used for portable radio and television; excessively small roller, needle, and ball bearings used for such equipment as air-turbine dental drills.

Epoxy missile resin—used for plastic tooling, metal bonding, adhesive, and casting and laminating applications.

Silicones for motor insulation and subzero lubricants—used in new glassmaking techniques for myriad products.

Ribbon glass for capacitors—used widely in electronics field.

Radar bulbs—used in air-traffic control equipment.

Ribbon cable for missiles—used in the communications industry.

Automatic gun cameras—used in banks, toll booths, and so on.

Fluxless aluminum soldering—used for kitchen-utensil repair, gutters, flashings, antennas, electrical joints, auto repairing, farm machinery, and so on.

Lightweight hydraulic pumps—used in automated machinery and pneumatic control systems.

Voice-interruption priority system—used for assembly-line production control.

Examples such as the foregoing, it might be pointed out, do not generally emphasize an area in which space exploration is making one of its greatest contributions. This is the creation of new materials, metals, fabrics, alloys, and compounds that are finding their way rapidly into the commercial market.*

One other area of by-products has not been mentioned—namely, research into food and food products. This research covers an especially wide range, from simple means of preservation and packaging of food, to entirely new food sources. An example of the latter is the research on *Chlorella*, a single-celled freshwater alga, which first attracted attention as a producer of oxygen for breathing. Since the algae, in the process of producing oxygen from carbon dioxide and sunlight, multiply, the question of what to do with the surplus algae arose. The

* *The Practical Values of Space Exploration*, Report of the Committee on Sciences and Astronautics (87th Congress, 1st Session, House of Representatives, House Report No. 1276), August 1961, pp. 43–49.

thought, first jokingly uttered, that one way of getting rid of the surplus consisted of eating it, turned out to be literally right. Chlorella is edible, and a fair amount of work has been spent in devising meals based on Chlorella.

At one time in the future there will be a colony on the moon, and it is hoped, of course, that this colony will be able to supply its own food needs. Hence, some research has been started on plants that are edible and that probably can be grown on the moon in enclosed spaces. It is more than likely that one of the strains developed for the moon colony will prove of value here on the earth, too.

EPILOGUE   The Race for Space

In the days—it is a question of less than a decade, though it feels like "long ago"—before Tiros televised pictures of whole hurricanes from space and Telstar I transmitted television programs between the United States and Europe, many taxpayers had their own explanation for spending money on space research. It was somewhat simplified, but it was essentially correct, if incomplete. We couldn't let the Russians take over beyond the atmosphere, the reasoning ran; we might dislike the expenditure but since the Russians had somehow acquired a head start in the race for space we had to catch up.

Thus, the term "space race" was coined and though official Washington for the last few months of the year 1957 and through most of the year 1958 insisted that we were *not* in a space race with the Russians, the simple fact is that we were and still are. There are two aspects to this race. The first is purely military.

Congress recognized the fact when it passed the National Aeronautics and Space Act of 1958 and directed that "activities peculiar to or primarily associated with the development of weapons systems, military operations, or the defense of the United States . . . shall be the responsibility of, and shall be directed by, the Department of Defense." [1] In amendments to the Space Act proposed in

212

1960 and 1961, this directive was strengthened. "The Department of Defense shall undertake such activities in space, and such research and development connected therewith, as may be necessary for the defense of the United States." [2]

It is possible to argue, and indeed it has been argued, that ballistic missiles such as IRBMs (Intermediate Range Ballistic Missile, with a range of about 1,500 miles) and ICBMs (Intercontinental Ballistic Missile, with a range of 4,000 miles or more) are not really "space" weapons, that they are simply an extension of the traditional art of artillery. The argument appears to be largely a semantic one. Such missiles do traverse space, they are guided through space, and they employ the same engines and principles that are presently used for purposes of scientific exploration. While more advanced "space" weapons may evolve in the future, the missile as we know it today cannot very well be divorced from our thinking about space and its practical uses.

Going on this assumption, and casting an eye in the direction of the Iron Curtain, it is obvious that the Soviet Union is going all out to exploit space for military purposes.

Military men have known for years that the tremendously powerful booster the Soviets have been using to launch their massive Sputniks was originally designed to carry the primitive heavy version of the A-bomb across continents.

If there was ever doubt of the extent to which the Soviets intend to make space a selected medium for military purposes it was erased when Premier Khrushchev made his address to the Supreme Soviet on January 14, 1960. He commented in part:

> Our state has at its disposal powerful rocket equipment. The military air force and navy have lost their previous importance in view of the modern development of military equipment. This type of armament is not being reduced but replaced. Almost the entire military air force is being replaced by rocket equipment. We have by now sharply cut, and it seems will continue sharply to cut and even discontinue the manufacture of bombers and other obsolete equipment. In the navy, the submarine fleet assumes great importance, while surface ships can no longer play the part they once did. In our country the armed forces have been to a considerable extent transferred to rocket and nuclear arms. These arms are being perfected and will continue to be perfected until they are banned.

While it is difficult to assess the actual extent of the Soviet preoccupation with missiles—and the 1961 Tushino air show indicated strongly that the U.S.S.R. has not abandoned belief in the effectiveness of aircraft—it has been reported that the Russians are building upward of 100 IRBM and ICBM bases to be manned by about 200,000 men. Most of these, at least the intermediate range bases, are said to be along Russia's Baltic coast, in East Germany, in the southern Ukraine, and in the Carpathian Mountains.[3]

In any event, the space age is clearly "here" so far as the military are concerned, and U.S. forces—particularly since the development of the much lighter atomic warheads—

have been likewise diligent in their space efforts. This is because many military minds are now agreed that:[4]

We are moving inevitably into a time of astropower [the power to strike from space]. We face a threat beyond imagination, should events ever lead to open conflict in a world of hypersonic velocities and a raging atom chained as our slave. We must be strong, we must be able to change to meet change. What may come against our beloved America will not be signaled by one light from the North Church steeple, if they come by land, or two, if they come by sea. Never again. They will come through space, and their light of warning will be the blinding terror of a thermonuclear fireball.

It is important to note, in connection with military matters, that pure rocket power is not the only avenue to success in space use. The American Atlas missile, for example, which can carry a nuclear warhead and which operates on considerably less thrust than the powerful Soviet boosters thus far demonstrated, has nevertheless shown the capability of negotiating a 9,000-mile trek and landing in the target area. This is about 1,500 miles farther than any Soviet shots revealed to the public in the 3-year period following the first Sputnik. It is also a sufficient range to permit reaching almost any likely target on the globe.

From the military point of view, the meaning thus brought out is that sophistication of missiles together with reliability and ease of handling may be more important than pure power. For this reason, American advances in solid-propellant fuels—such as that used by the Army's Pershing (a missile for tactile range up to 200 miles), the

Navy's Polaris (IRBM), and the Air Force's Minuteman (ICBM)—are significant indeed. It means that U.S. missile technology may well be the most effective in existence.*

One of the reasons why many American citizens were, and still are, convinced that the space race is mainly, if not exclusively, a military matter is that the military aspect is so easy to explain. Anybody can understand that we must be able to shoot as far and as effectively as a potential enemy. However, the second aspect of the space race, that of international prestige, is also worthy of consideration.

Only recently has the full impact and meaning of this phase of our national space program come to be widely recognized. It has been stated, perhaps in its most forceful and succinct form, by an American official in a unique position to know. The former Director of the U.S. Information Agency, part of whose job is to keep track of the esteem in which America is held abroad, has told Congress: [5]

> Our space program may be considered as a measure of our vitality and our ability to compete with a formidable rival and as a criterion of our ability to maintain technological eminence worthy of emulation by other people.

This element of space exploration takes on particular significance in light of the current international struggle to influence the minds of men, in light of the rising tide of nationalism throughout the world, and in light of the intensification of the cold war as demonstrated by the

---

* *The Practical Values of Space Exploration,* Report of the Committee on Science and Astronautics (87th Congress, 1st Session, House of Representatives, House Report No. 1276), August 1961, pp. 11–13.

famous U-2 incident in [1960], the hardening attitude of Oriental communism, and the continuing East-West crises that break out around the globe at frequent intervals.

In the words of an influential newspaper: [6]

Wholly apart from the intellectual compulsions that now drive man to move higher and higher into the high heavens, it seems clear that our country can be niggardly in this field only at the risk of being completely and forever outclassed by Russia—a gamble that could have the most fearful political, economic, and military consequences.

Incidentally, there is another prestige factor to be considered. This is what might be called the chain-reaction factor: the likelihood that technological pre-eminence in the space field will attract top talent from other parts of the world to the banner of the country that develops it, and thus constantly nourish and replenish the efforts of that country. It is a consideration that has not received general attention, although it has been discussed before some of the world's loading space scientists.[7]

Here again, as with the military situation, the Soviets are making every effort to exploit their dexterity in space. They are pursuing the prestige gambit directly and indirectly. In the first category, for example, they give top priority to space exhibits in important public forums—as their duplicate Sputniks strategically placed at the World's Fair and the United Nations attest. Premier Khrushchev's delight in making gifts to foreigners of miniature Soviet pennants similar to that carried in Lunik II—which hit the moon—is another instance. The worldwide "good will" tours of the Soviet astronauts, following their exploits in space, are yet another.

The indirect drive for prestige via space technology is far more important. It has been described by a congressional committee as follows: [8]

It is difficult to escape the conclusion that the Soviet Union in the last several years has demonstrated a great skill in co-ordinating its progress in missilery, its success in space missions, and its foreign policy and world image. Shots seem to have been timed to maximize the effects of visits of Soviet leaders and to punctuate Soviet statements and positions in international negotiations. This is not to equate their space activities with hollow propaganda. Empty claims do not have a positive effect for long. Nor is there any firm evidence that it has been possible for political policymakers to call their shots at times inconsistent with good scientific and technical needs. The conclusion is rather that the many elements of scientific, technical, military, political, and psychological policy are all weighed, and tests which make a full contribution to such a combined strategy are carried out and supported with appropriate publicity.

There is also evidence that scientific endeavor by the Russians for prestige purposes is having repercussions on internal policy. Great emphasis is currently being placed on the demonstrable usefulness of scientific effort—to the extent that Soviet colleges, research institutions, examining boards, and academies of science have been directed to be more exacting in conferring scientific degrees and titles. Newness and usefulness are requisite, but, at the same time, degrees may now be awarded for other than dissertations; inventions and textbooks of major importance may also earn a degree for their authors.

Within the prestige context, it is true that the United States must labor under certain handicaps because of the nature of its democratic system.

No effort is made in the American space program to hide the details. Our astronauts blast off from Cape Canaveral under the very nose of the television cameras. Our burn-ups, misfires, explosions, fizzles, and lost or wayward vehicles are well publicized. Those of the Soviet Union rarely are. Even though most nations are well aware that the Russians must be having their troubles, too, the appearance of the uniform success fostered by the U.S.S.R. inevitably contributes to an image of scientific superiority.[9] In addition, the Soviets have developed a habit of striving for spectacular "firsts," most of which undoubtedly are undertaken almost as much for prestige reasons as for scientific ones.

Still, the United States has done well from the prestige angle. So far as the world's scientific fraternity is concerned, it may even be in the lead.

In the first 40 or so months following the opening of the space age, as signaled by the launching of Sputnik I in October 1957, the United States put 46 satellites into orbit out of 88 attempts. Two out of 5 deep-space probes were successful. The degree of success for all major launchings ran better than 50 per cent. The American effort has been based on a broad scope of inquiry and includes long-range communications, weather reporting, navigation and surveillance vehicles, as well as information-gathering satellites.

During the same period the Soviets launched 12 earth satellites, 2 deep-space probes, 1 lunar-impact probe, and 1 satellite into a much elongated earth orbit that circled and photographed the moon. Most of their vehicles have been substantially heavier than those launched by the United States. They launched some 55 tons of space vehicles compared to about 25 tons for the United States. However, complete information on their scientific purposes and the results obtained have never been disclosed.

The orbital flight of Major Yuri Gagarin, the first human into space, on April 12, 1961, was not only a spectacular scientific feat it contributed a great deal to the prestige of the Soviet Union—as did the subsequent extended orbital flight of Gherman Titov on August 6, 1961. The suborbital flights of American astronauts Alan Shepard on May 5, 1961, and Virgil Grissom on July 21, 1961, have had a similar effect on behalf of this country. While the American effort in manned space flight may trail that of the Russians, the U.S. demonstrations of scientific and utilitarian projects, such as the Explorer and Pioneer programs and the meteorological, navigation, and communication-satellite systems, have their own unique influence upon the international community. This fact has been typified by Echo I, the 100-foot sphere whose brilliant and consistent voyage through the heavens has been witnessed by millions and which stands out as the brightest manmade star in the firmament.

In addition the United States has sought the cooperation of scientists and facilities in other countries to aid in the prosecution of its space program. It has made free to all a wealth of scientific information resulting from its programs, and it has encouraged the growth of the European Space Development Agency, which represents a pooling of the talent and resources of a number of free-world countries anxious to join in the space-exploration adventure. It has invited nations around the globe to participate in its communication-satellite program. This, too, has had a special kind of effect, one felt principally, perhaps, in the technical echelons, but one as yet unmatched by the Soviets.

The world political value of such factors cannot be discounted. To the extent that the welfare of the United States depends upon its stature in the eyes of the rest of the world (which is believed considerable) and to the extent that the scientific capability of the United States influences such stature (which is also believed considerable) our space venture has very marked practical utility. It may even mean the difference between freedom and dictatorship, between survival and oblivion.*

The space race, however, should not be compared to a simple race such as is run by men during the Olympics and by horses on the race track. There, the first man, or the first horse, "wins" and that is the end of the race. In the space race all the work begins *after* it has been "won." "Getting to the moon first" is just the introduction to what is to follow.

It is important to recognize that "getting there first" is only one part of the race. Two other parts are just as crucial:

1. What will we learn from our effort to explore beyond the earth?

* *The Practical Values of Space Exploration, op. cit.*, pp. 16–18.

2. How will we use this knowledge after it is acquired?

There is very little doubt that the first nation to put a man on the moon is going to reap enormous political and psychological benefits from the feat *per se*. It is most desirable that the United States be that nation—if not in respect to the moon, then in respect to Mars or Venus or other planets.

But neither is there much doubt that "getting there first" will result only in transient glory unless scientific knowledge of a high order is acquired in the process and is put to good use. The nation or group of nations that wins the race in point of time, and fails in the other categories, is likely to receive the Hollywood treatment of a bursting gala "premiere," but eventually to find itself displaced by the late-bloomers who make their investigation count. The Vikings had the technique to get to the New World "first," but England, France, and Spain won the prizes.

It is a lesson that the United States and Russia, as well as the European nations now pooling their resources in space exploration, might be wise to keep in mind.

If, for example, our exploration contributes to a true understanding of the origin of the universe and, coincidentally, the ultimate destiny of man—this may prove to be of such tremendous significance in human affairs as to dwarf completely the means by which the revelations were obtained or when the observations leading to them were made. With no intent to deprecate the notable achievements of the Soviet Union in space research, it can nonetheless be said that the broad scope of the American effort has—thus far at least—been outstanding in scientific results. And, as subsequent parts of this report suggest, our free-enterprise system has been quick to take advantage of the technological fallout.

In summary, our international prestige and stature, so far as they are influenced by our space activities, depend on all 3 elements of "the race"—not on 1 or 2.

A natural outgrowth of the military and prestige facets of space exploration is the question of whether this activity, in time, will replace the forces that have historically driven nations into armed conflict.

Any number of social scientists and historians have speculated that this might occur. The theory is that the conquest of space may prove to be the moral equivalent of war by substituting for certain material and psychological needs usually supplied through war; that the absorption of energies, resources, imagination, and aggressiveness in pursuit of the space adventure may become an effective way of maintaining peace.

Put another way, nations might become "extroverted" to the point where their urge to overcome the unknown would dwarf their historic desires for power, wealth, and recognition—attributes that have so often led to war in the past.

The fact that the United Nations, late in 1959, agreed to set up a permanent Committee on the Peaceful Uses of Outer Space attests to the hopes and potential of such a development.

Of course, whether this condition will actually develop is anybody's guess. But in a world where brute force is becoming increasingly dangerous and catastrophic, the bare possibility of such a result should not be ignored by those who may be contemplating the values of space exploration. It could be the highest value of them all.*

But neither the talk about the space race, nor the cost accounting in dollars and cents regarding the monetary value of communication satellites, must obscure the ultimate fact that space exploration is simply progress. Quite a number of years ago, in 1946, Arthur C. Clarke, speaking to the members of the British Interplanetary Society in London, said ". . . our civilization is no more than the sum of all the dreams that earlier ages have brought to fulfillment. And so it must always be, for if men cease to dream, if they turn their backs upon the wonder of the universe, the story of our race will be coming to an end." †

In any endeavor as futuristic as space exploration, it is not difficult to become lost in the land of the starry-eyed prognosticators. Conversely, it is also easy to find oneself lining up with the debunkers and the champions of the status quo, for their arguments and views give the impression of being hardheaded, sensible.

If one must err in either direction, however, it is probably safer, where space is concerned, to err in the direction of the enthusiasts. This is because . . .the nation cannot afford not to be in the vanguard of the space explorers.

Events today move with facility and lightning rapidity. Today, more than ever, time is on the side of the expeditious. We can no lonker take the risk of giving much support to the scoffers—to that breed of unimaginative souls who thought Robert Fulton [1765–1815] was a fool for

---

* *The Practical Values of Space Exploration, op. cit.,* p. 22.
† Published later in *The Challenge of the Spaceships,* New York, Harper and Row, 1955, p. 15.

harnessing a paddlewheel to a boiler, who thought Henry Ford [1863–1947] was a fool for putting an internal combustion engine on wheels, who thought Samuel Langley [1834–1906] was a fool for designing a contraption to fly through the air.

There are always those who will say it cannot be done. Even in this era of sophisticated flight there have been those who said the sound barrier would never be broken. It was. Others said later that space vehicles would never get through the heat barrier. They have. Now, some say men will never overcome the radiation barrier in space. But we can be sure they will.

It is undoubtedly wise for the layman, in terms of the benefits he can expect from the space program in the foreseeable future, to steer a reasonable course between the two extremes. Yet one cannot help remembering that the secret of taking practical energy from the atom, a secret the human race had been trying to learn for thousands of years, was accomplished in less than a decade from the moment when men first determined that it was possible to split an atom. It is difficult to forget that even after World War II some of our most respected scientists sold short the idea of developing long-range missiles. Impractical, they said; visionary. But 6 years after the United States went to work seriously on missiles, an operational ICBM with a 9,000-mile range was an accomplished fact.

All the glowing predictions being made on behalf of space exploration will not be here tomorrow or the next day. Yet this seems less important than that we recognize the significance of our moment of history.

We may think of that moment as a new age—the age of

space and the atom—to follow the historic ages of stone, bronze, and iron. We may think of it in terms of theories of succeeding from those of Copernicus [1473–1543] to those of Newton [1642–1727] and thence to Freud [1856–1939] and now Einstein [1879–1955]. We may think of our time as the time of exploiting the new fourth state of matter: plasma or the ion. Or we may think of it in terms of revolutions, as passing from the industrial cycle of steam through the railroad-steel cycle, through the electricity-automobile cycle, into the burgeoning technological revolution of today.

However we think of it, it is a dawning period and one that—in its scope and potential—promises to dwarf much of what has gone before. Those who have given careful thought to the matter are convinced that while some caution is in order, the new era is not one to be approached with timidity, inhibited imagination, or too much convention. Neither is there any point in trying to hold off the tempo of this oncoming age or, in any other way, to evade it.

Mark Twain [1835–1910] once listened to the complaints of an old riverboat pilot who was having trouble making the switch from sail to steam. The old pilot wanted no part of the newfangled steam contraptions. "Maybe so," replied Twain, "but when it's steamboat time, you steam."

Today is space time and man is going to explore it.*

---

* *The Practical Values of Space Exploration, op. cit.,* pp. 23–25.

REFERENCES

1. Public Law 85-568, 85th Congress.

2. House Report No. 1633, 86th Congress, 2d Session, p. 6; House Report No. 747, 87th Congress, 1st Session, p. 7.

3. Associated Press dispatch, dateline London, December 2, 1959.

4. Brigadier General Robert L. Scott USAF (retired), *Space Age,* February 1959, p. 63.

5. George V. Allen, testimony before the House Committee on Science and Astronautics, January 22, 1960.

6. An editorial in the Washington [D.C.] *Evening Star,* April 4, 1960.

7. Remarks of Hon. Aubrey Jones, Minister of Supply, to the International Astronautical Federation, London, September 1, 1959.

8. *Space, Missiles, and the Nation,* Report of the House Committee on Science and Astronautics, May 18, 1960, p. 53.

9. Even this appearance is not flawless. Spacecraft I, which the Soviets launched in May 1960, with the intent of returning it to the earth, went awry and remains in an unplanned orbit. The Venus probe the Soviets launched in February 1961, which was intended to broadcast technical data en route to the vicinity of the planet, failed when only several million miles from the earth and has been lost.

Appendixes

I A Listing of U. S. Rockets with Space Capability

Boosters

Vanguard. The first rocket specifically designed for orbiting scientific payloads during the International Geophysical Year. Its first stage was based on the earlier Viking rockets of the U. S. Navy (liquid fuel). The second stage, developed specifically for this purpose, was also liquid fuel (hypergolic combination), while the third stage was solid fuel. The length of the rocket was 70 feet, take-off weight around 18,000 pounds, and the payload capacity 20.5 pounds (maximum) for a low orbit. Higher payloads were carried late in the program with the aid of improved upper stages.

Redstone. The Redstone rocket was based on the German V-2 and originally developed by the Army to carry very heavy warheads over a range of 200 miles. It was 69 feet, 6 inches long with a take-off weight of about 60,000 pounds. When the next larger rocket, the Jupiter, was to be developed, a number of Redstone rockets were set aside to test components for the Jupiter. These Redstones were labeled Jupiter-C and carried a 3-stage assembly of solid-fuel rockets. It was one of the Jupiter-C rockets that put the first American satellite, Explorer I, into orbit. The Redstone was also used for the two suborbital flights of the Mercury capsule.

Jupiter. This liquid-fuel rocket is normally a 1,500-mile missile. It is 58 feet long with a take-off weight of 105,000 pounds. Equipped with extra upper stages, the Jupiter rocket, under the name "Juno" has been used as a booster for early American lunar probes.

Thor. This is also a liquid-fuel rocket, developed by the Air Force, with a 1,500 mile range. Sixty-five feet in length, it has a take-off weight of 110,000 pounds. The Thor has been used as a booster for many artificial satellites.

Scout. This 4-stage solid-fuel rocket is used by both the Navy (the Sea Scout) and the Air Force (the Blue Scout). Some of the stages are rockets originally developed for other designs— for example, early versions of the Polaris missile. The Scout can place satellites weighing up to 200 pounds into a 300-mile orbit.

Saturn. The Saturn booster has been designed specifically for the purpose of boosting very heavy payloads into space. The bottom stage (the only one that has had test flights) is over 90 feet long; its 8 engines (4 are mounted rigidly, 4 are swivel-mounted) develop together a take-off thrust of 1.3 million pounds. The engines are the same which propel the Jupiter and Thor missiles.

Atlas. This Intercontinental missile's 3 engines develop a take-off thrust of 360,000 pounds. With a take-off weight of 260,000 pounds, the missile is 82 feet long. It has been used for heavy satellites and, of course, for the orbital flights with the Mercury capsule.

Titan. The 2 engines of this intercontinental missile develop a take-off thrust of 220,000 pounds. The missile is almost precisely 100 feet long. The Titan has not been used for satellite work yet, but its later versions, Titan II and Titan III, will play a role in the space program.

ꊸ Upper Stages

Solid-fuel cluster. This cluster, used in combination with the Redstone to make Jupiter-C, consists of a scaled-down version of the solid-fuel Sergeant rocket. The 3-stage cluster consisted of 11 of these rockets for the first stage; they were arranged in a circle with a hole in the center into which the second stage, consisting of 5 rockets, fitted. The third stage (the front end of which was the Explorer satellite) was a single rocket of the same type, standing on top of the second stage.

Able. One of the first liquid-fuel rockets specifically developed as a top stage for space work, at sea level it produces a thrust of 7,800 pounds, with a burning time of 120 seconds. The AbleStar is a development of the Able; its thrust is 8,000 pounds and the burning time 300 seconds. AbleStar can be shut off at any time and restarted in orbit.

Delta. A much-used upper stage for liquid-fuel rockets, the Delta's performance characteristics are similar to that of Able.

Agena. A large upper-stage rocket, extensively used by the Air Force for its polar-orbiting Discoverer satellites, the Agena has a thrust of 15,500 pounds and a burning time of 120 seconds. Agena-B is a larger version developing 16,000 pounds of thrust for 240 seconds. Like AbleStar, the Agena-B is capable of being started in space.

A number of upper stages for the Saturn booster are under development but have not yet reached final form.

II Chronology of Meteorological-
Ⓜ   Satellite Events

March 7, 1947. The first successful photographs of clouds from a height greater than 100 miles were obtained by the twentieth V-2 rocket to be launched in America (White Sands, New Mexico).

January 1949. Major Delmar L. Crowson pointed to the meteorological potentialities of rocket photographs or television in an article, "Cloud Observations from Rockets," in the *Bulletin of the American Meteorological Society.*

April 1951. S. M. Greenfield and W. W. Kellogg, in a USAF Project Rand Report, now declassified, presented a feasibility study on weather reconnaissance from a satellite vehicle.

September 1954. Formal plans were laid for an International Geophysical Year at the 10th General Assembly of the International Union of Geodesy and Geophysics, Rome, Italy. The plans included high atmospheric soundings by means of rockets.

October 5, 1954. Interest in high-altitude cloud photography was stimulated by the photographic depiction of the cloud system of an unsuspected tropical storm near Del

Rio, Texas. Photographs were obtained from 2 rocket-borne movie cameras launched as part of a naval-research program at White Sands, New Mexico.

1955. The United States undertook a scientific data-gathering satellite project as part of its contribution to the IGY. Each of the military services submitted plans to the Secretary of Defense. The result—Project Vanguard—was a triservice effort, under the direction of the Office of Naval Research.

"Project Vanguard" was more than just a rocket or a satellite; it was a system, a complete and totally integrated space program. In addition to development of the vehicle itself, it provided a world-wide tracking system, both radio and optical, and the launching system to place the satellite in orbit.[1]

July 29, 1955. The National Academy of Sciences and the National Science Foundation announced that the United States was planning to construct an earth satellite that would be launched during the IGY. These organizations would sponsor the project with assistance from the Department of Defense, which would furnish the equipment and facilities. The program was to be carried out under the IGY program with the data made available to the international scientific community.

April 1956. The Committee on Meteorology (now the Committee on Atmospheric Sciences) was established by the National Academy of Sciences–National Research Council.

January 25, 1958. In its interim report, *Research and Education in Meteorology*, the Committee on Meteorology of the National Academy of Sciences–National Research Council recommended establishment of a National Institute of Atmospheric Research.

February 1958. The University Committee on Atmospheric Research (UCAR) was established. The UCAR became the University Corporation for Atmospheric Research in the spring of 1959.

February 1958. The Satellite Meteorology Branch was established by the Geophysics Research Directorate, Air Force Cambridge Research Center.

February 12, 1958. Public Law 85-325 authorized the Secretary of Defense to engage in advanced projects in the field of research and development for weapons systems, and for 1 year to engage in nonmilitary advanced space projects as designated by the President.

February 14, 1958. Basic Objectives of a Continuing Program of Scientific Research in Outer Space, a report by the Technical Panel of the Earth Satellite Program of the U.S. National Committee for the IGY, was published. The report proposed a program of space research extending beyond the IGY. It outlined the technical investigations that should be made by sounding rockets, lightweight and advanced satellites, lunar probes, planetary and interplanetary research, and manned space flight, and gave a detailed description of the scientific information that could be gained from these experiments.

March 19, 1958. The IGY Satellite Panel offered a space program for the United States.

March 26, 1958. "Introduction to Outer Space," an explanatory statement prepared by the President's Science Advisory Committee, described the ways in which satellites might be used for meteorological purposes and stated:

> The satellite that will turn its attention downward holds great promise for meteorology and the eventual improvement of weather forecasting.

April 2, 1958. President Eisenhower in a message to Congress proposed the establishment of a National Aeronautics and Space Agency to have responsibility for civilian space science and aeronautical activities and of a National Aeronautics and Space Board to assist the President and the Director of the National Aeronautics and Space Agency.

May 1958. ARPA's Committee on Meteorological Satellites began its initial planning of Tiros.

June 1958. The National Academy of Sciences established the Space Science Board, one of whose committees was the Committee on Meteorological Aspects of Satellites.

July 1958. The National Science Foundation established an Atmospheric Sciences Program within its Division of Mathematical, Physical, and Engineering Sciences.

July 29, 1958. The National Aeronautics and Space Act of 1958 (Public Law 85-568) was signed by President Eisenhower. The act established the National Aeronautics and Space Administration (NASA) to have responsibility for and direct "aeronautical and space activities sponsored by the United States, except activities peculiar to or primarily associated with the development of weapons systems, military operations, or the defense of the United

States (including the research and development necessary to make effective provision for the defense of the United States) . . . ," which were to be placed under the authority of the Department of Defense [DOD]. The functions, facilities, and personnel of the National Advisory Committee for Aeronautics were to be transferred to NASA, and the President was given authority for 4 years to transfer related functions from other agencies. The act directed the President to "develop a comprehensive program of aeronautical and space activities to be conducted by agencies of the United States," to assign responsibility for these activities, and to provide for "effective" NASA–DOD cooperation. He was to be assisted in these duties by the advisory National Aeronautics and Space Council.

September 26, 1958. An attempt was made to launch Vanguard satellite-launching vehicle III, the first satellite to carry equipment designed to measure cloud cover. It failed to orbit.

October 1, 1958. NASA's first day of business. The President issued Executive Order No. 10783, which transferred to it several Department of Defense projects whose paramount objectives were of a nonmilitary nature. Among these was the scientific satellite program, including Project Vanguard, which had been under the direction of the Department of the Navy since 1955.

Among NASA's responsibilities were the design and procurement of vehicles and satellite payloads, the launching and monitoring of scientific satellites, the accumulation and reduction of data, and the carrying on of programs of basic and applied research in support of space science and technology.

October 28, 1958. The Meteorological Satellite Section (later Laboratory) was established by the Weather Bureau.

November 1958. The Committee on Space Research (COSPAR), a committee organized by the International Council of Scientific Unions (ICSU), had its first meeting in London.

February 17, 1959. Vanguard II, carrying two photocell units to measure reflected sunlight, was launched from Cape Canaveral. Its instruments were developed by the Army Signal Corps Research and Development Laboratories at Fort Monmouth, New Jersey. The feasibility of a weather satellite was demonstrated by this experiment.

March 1959. Dr. Richard W. Porter, the U.S. delegate to COSPAR at its meeting at The Hague [the Netherlands], conveyed an offer of the United States to carry the experiments of scientists of other nations in our space vehicles. This offer was reaffirmed at the COSPAR meetings held in Nice, France, January 1960.

April 8, 1959. Representatives of the National Aeronautics and Space Administration and the Weather Bureau testified on the meteorological satellite program in a hearing on the NASA authorization for the fiscal year 1960 held by the NASA Authorization Subcommittee of the Senate Committee on Aeronautical and Space Sciences.

April 13, 1959. Project Tiros was transferred from the Department of Defense to the National Aeronautics and Space Administration.

April 23, 1959. The Joint Meteorological Satellite Advisory Committee was established.

April–May 1959. At the direction of the Third Congress

of the World Meteorological Organization, its executive committee established the Panel of Experts on Artificial Satellites.

July 1959. The Interdepartmental Committee on Atmospheric Sciences was established as a Committee of the Federal Council for Science and Technology.

August 7, 1959. Explorer VI was launched. It transmitted a rough picture of the earth's surface and cloud cover, which, while crude, demonstrated that cloud photography covering large areas by means of satellites was possible.

August 24, 1959. Pictures taken over the Caribbean Sea and the Atlantic Ocean from the nose cone of an Atlas missile showed the potential of high-altitude photography for providing meteorologists with pictures of cloud patterns over large areas.

October 13, 1959. Explorer VII was launched. It contained instrumentation originally planned for use during the IGY, including the first satellite radiation-balance experiment. The radiation instrumentation was designed by Professor Verner E. Suomi, of the University of Wisconsin.

October 26, 1959. Senator Wiley, of Wisconsin, proposed that the United States put into orbit an "international weatherman" satellite to collect and give out weather data to the entire world.

November 4, 1959. The International Council of Scientific Unions (ICSU) established the International Geophysics Committee (CIG) to succeed the Special Committee on the International Geophysical Year (CSAGI) in order to continue the IGY pattern of world cooperation in geophysical matters.

November 12–13, 1959. The WMO Panel of Experts on Artificial Satellites held its first meeting in Geneva, Switzerland.

January 11, 1960. The First International Space Science Symposium opened at Nice, France.

April 1, 1960. Tiros I, the first fully equipped meteorological satellite, was successfully launched. It had a useful operating lifetime of 78 days, during which period a total of almost 23,000 cloud pictures were transmitted.

April 1, 1960. Tiros I proved its usefulness for sea-ice reconnaissance by depicting ice conditions in the Gulf of St. Lawrence.

April 3, 1960. The first Tiros operational nephanalysis [cloud analysis] was transmitted.

April 10, 1960. Tiros I proved the utility of the meteorological satellite in hurricane tracking and detection by picking up a tropical cyclone centered in the South Pacific north of New Zealand.

April 1960. Initial Tiros results were presented to the American Meteorological Society–American Geophysical Union meeting in Washington, D.C.

May 10, 1960. The timing mechanism that controlled remote operation of the narrow-angle camera on Tiros I resumed operation after having failed to respond to commands since April 2.

May 19, 1960. Tiros I suggested its potential use in tornado forecasting by photographing an unusual "square cloud" formation that subsequently produced tornadoes over Oklahoma.

June 27, 1960. The National Science Foundation and the University Corporation for Atmospheric Research announced the appointment of Dr. Walter Orr Roberts as Director of the National Center for Atmospheric Research and the grant of $500,000 by the NSF to the UCAR to be used in establishment of the center.

June 29, 1960. The decision was made to discontinue attempts to interrogate Tiros I after orbit 1,302 over Fort Monmouth, New Jersey. The wide-angle camera and all telemetry had ceased to function although beacons continued operating.

June 30, 1960. Meteorology on the Move, a progress report of the Committee on Atmospheric Sciences of the National Academy of Sciences–National Research Council pointed out that "there exists at the moment no organization or group in the world that is prepared to exploit fully the new wealth of information that meteorological satellites will certainly provide" and urged prompt creation of the proposed National Center for Atmospheric Research "to supply the basic scientific research and guidance" to meet this need.

August 1960. NASA and the Weather Bureau jointly sent invitations to scientists in 21 nations, including the Soviet Union, to participate in the analysis of weather information to be gathered by Tiros II.

September 13, 1960. The Aeronautics and Astronautics Coordinating Board was officially established by agreement between NASA and the DOD. The Unmanned Spacecraft Panel of this Board provides policy-level coordination for the meteorological satellite program.

September 22, 1960. President Eisenhower in an address to the United Nations proposed that:

We press forward with a program of international cooperation for constructive peaceful uses of outer space under the United Nations. Better weather forecasting, improved worldwide communications . . . are but a few of the benefits of such cooperation.

October 10, 1960. It was decided at a high-level meeting of officials of NASA, the Department of Commerce, the Federal Aviation Agency, and the Department of Defense that plans should be made for a national operational meteorological satellite system.

October 18, 1960. Universities were briefed by NASA and the Weather Bureau on Tiros data and results.

November 23, 1960. Tiros II was successfully launched. It had essentially the same configuration as Tiros I. However, Tiros II had, in addition, nonscanning and scanning infrared equipment to provide measurements of the atmospheric heat budget, and it contained magnetic attitude control of spin axis not contained by Tiros I. The brilliance of the performance was dulled slightly by the fact that the wide-angle camera did not perform satisfactorily. The resulting pictures were, therefore, not of the same quality as those from Tiros I, but were used by the meteorologists to produce nephanalyses.

November 23, 1960. A balloon, carrying an instrument package to check on radiation at heights to 112,000 feet, was launched from Sioux Falls, South Dakota. The radiation data obtained are to be compared with similar data obtained from Tiros II.

November 28, 1960. The National Aeronautics and Space Administration held an industry briefing on the integration and test contract for construction of the advanced meteorological satellite, Nimbus.

December 1960. The Panel on Operational Meteorological Satellites (POMS) came into existence.

January 6, 1961. It was announced by the Navy that Thompson Ramo–Wooldridge, Inc., had developed a prototype television camera and transmitting station which could be used for the immediate transmission of live high-altitude pictures as contrasted with the still pictures transmitted by the Tiros satellites. The camera, placed in the nose of an Arcas (All-purpose Rocket for the Collection of Atmospheric Soundings) rocket, would broadcast as it was parachuted to earth from an altitude of 40 miles.

January 12, 1961. The *Report to the President-Elect of the Ad Hoc Committee on Space* (The Wiesner Report) was released. It pointed to the benefits of meteorological satellites and recommended both "a vigorous program to exploit the potentialities of practical space systems" and the establishment of "the organizational machinery within the government to administer an industry-government civilian space program."

January 13, 1961. The WMO announced that at the request of the United States it had distributed a notice to each of its member nations and territories stating that weather data from Tiros II was available to them for use in their meteorological services.

January 19, 1961. NASA temporarily suspended programing of the Tiros II wide-angle camera in order to alleviate threat of power failure.

January 30, 1961. In his State of the Union address President Kennedy announced his administration's intention to encourage international scientific cooperation, stating:

> Specifically, I now invite all nations—including the Soviet Union—to join with us in developing a weather-prediction program . . . .

February 7–10, 1961. The second meeting of the WMO Panel of Experts on Artificial Satellites was held in Washington, D.C. The Soviet member, Dr. Victor Bugaev, did not attend.

April 1961. The Panel on Operational Meteorological Satellites (POMS) of the National Coordinating Committee for Aviation Meteorology recommended that funds be made available for the development of a national operational meteorological satellite system "at the earliest possible date." Management responsibility for this system would be assigned to the Weather Bureau, wtih NASA carrying out the development and launching of Nimbus and Aeros spacecraft and the spacecraft control, programing, and tracking.

April 13, 1961. [Senate bill] 1577 was introduced by Senator Francis Case to create a National Weather Council and to provide coordination and central direction for an accelerated program of weather research.

April 18, 1961. The Brookings Institution report, *Proposed Studies on the Implications of Peaceful Space Activities for Human Affairs,* which had been prepared for the NASA Committee on Long-Range Studies and transmitted to it on November 30, 1960, was published as a House of Representatives report. The report contained a section, "Implications of a Space-Derived Weather Predicting System."

April 24, 1961. The President's Science Advisory Committee Ad Hoc Panel on Meteorological Satellites transmitted a memorandum on the POMS plan to Dr. Wiesner. The memorandum found the POMS plan "extremely timely and of unusual importance" and reached a number of technical conclusions.

May 10, 1961. Moscow *Tass* reported in English to Europe that Professor F. Davitaya had described the potentialities of outer space for meteorological purposes in an article in that day's *Selskaya Zhizn* ("Rural Life"). Tass continued:

> The Soviet scientist points out that plans are already afoot for determining the distribution of precipitation and thunderstorm areas by means of radar installed in satellite spaceships. There are also other possibilities of studying the Earth's atmosphere and processes occurring in it from spaceships. These possibilities are now the subject of preliminary studies.

May 11–30, 1961. The WMO Executive Committee, meeting in Geneva, Switzerland, approved a number of the recommendations of its Panel of Experts on Artificial Satellites.

May 25, 1961. In a message to Congress on urgent national needs, President Kennedy supported the plan of the Panel on Operational Meteorological Satellites by requesting an additional $75 million, including a $53 million appropriation for the Weather Bureau, to "help give us at the earliest possible time a satellite system for worldwide weather observation."

May 26–27, 1961. The First National Conference on the Peaceful Uses of Space, Tulsa, Oklahoma, included a session on applying space science to communications, weather, and navigation.

June–July, 1961. A series of planning conferences for the purpose of preparing a 10-year research program for meteorology was held by a group of meteorologists under the auspices of the National Academy of Sciences. Dr. Sverre Petterssen, The University of Chicago, served as the task-force director.

July 1961. Tiros I picture data were released through the National Weather Records Center.

July 12, 1961. Tiros III was launched from Cape Canaveral at 6:25 A.M. (e.d.t.). It is in orbit ranging from 460.74 to 506.52 miles and circles the globe every 100 minutes. The launching coincided with the advent of the 1961 hurricane season—a weather disturbance in the Atlantic could afford a quick test for Tiros III. On its first pass it transmitted 35 pictures showing cloud cover over Newfoundland, the Gulf of St. Lawrence, and the St. Lawrence Valley region.

July 19, 1961. Photographs of clouds obtained through meteorological satellite Tiros III revealed the location and configuration of a tropical cyclone a few hundred miles southwest of Los Angeles. This achievement was especially important because the storm developed in an area of sparse weather reports and with significant fishing operations; in fact, much of the time there were no reports from ships and no information of the storm except through

Tiros photographs, which gave more about the position, extent, and pattern of the cyclone than was obtainable from any other available sources.

July 23, 1961. Krasnaya Zvezda, newspaper of the Soviet armed forces, denounced the orbiting of Tiros III and Midas III, which had also been launched on July 12, as espionage by the United States. The newspaper charged:

> A spy is a spy no matter at what height it flies. The flights of the satellite spies over foreign territory are acts of aggression.

July 25–27, 1961. The House Committee on Science and Astronautics held hearings on the national meteorological satellite program.

August 8, 1961. The Tiros III international participation period began.

August 16, 1961. The Section on Meteorology of the American Geophysical Union established a Committee on Meteorological Satellites.

September 10, 1961. Tiros III spotted Hurricane "Esther" in the Atlantic 2 days before it could be surveyed by weather reconnaissance aircraft.

September 25, 1961. President Kennedy in an address to the United Nations again urged international cooperation in the use of outer space for meteorological purposes, stating:

> We shall further propose cooperative efforts between all nations in weather prediction and eventually in weather control.

September 29, 1961. In an address to the International Conference on Cloud Physics, Dr. Thomas F. Malone, president of the American Geophysical Union and of the American Meteorological Society, proposed establishing

> . . . within the framework of the International Council of Scientific Unions a committee which would be the equivalent of Cospar [Committee on Space Research] and Scor [Special Committee for Oceanic Research] and be the focal point for an international collaborative effort in atmospheric research for the scientific and academic community, complementing the function that the World Meteorological Organization provides for the national weather services . . . .

September 30, 1961. President Kennedy signed the Supplemental Appropriation Act, 1962 (Public Law 87-332), which appropriated $48 million to the Weather Bureau for meteorological satellite operations.

October 1961. The first of Tiros II infrared data were released for research use.

October 18, 1961. The House Committee on Science and Astronautics issued a report, *National Meteorological Satellite Program*, which called upon NASA and the Weather Bureau to

> . . . sign a formal agreement delineating the responsibilities of each agency for the national meteorological satellite program . . . .

October 19, 1961. The Atmospheric Sciences, 1961–71, a study prepared under the auspices of the National Academy of Sciences–National Research Council, was transmitted to Dr. Jerome B. Wiesner.

October 22, 1961. The Twentieth American Assembly at Arden House, Harriman, New York, on "Outer Space: Prospects for Man and Society" reached general agreement on a final report, which included among its recommendations:

> We urge that the United Nations and its specialized agencies be given increased responsibilities with respect to international communication and weather satellite systems.

October 22, 1961. In an address at St. Louis University, Harlan Cleveland, Assistant Secretary of State for International Organization Affairs, stated:

> Our goal is to preserve peace in outer space—and extend to all nations the benefits of exploring it. We will in this assembly propose concrete methods to this end—
> A world weather watch using satellites and other advance techniques;
> A cooperative search for ways by which man can start modifying the weather; . . .

November 13–22, 1961. NASA and the Weather Bureau held an International Meteorological Satellite Workshop in Washington, D.C. Twenty-seven nations sent representatives to this workshop, whose purpose was to instruct foreign meteorologists on the techniques of interpreting weather-satellite data. There were no representatives from the Soviet Union, Czechoslovakia, or Poland, which had previously accepted invitations to the workshop.

November 23, 1961. Tiros II completed 1 year in orbit with most systems still functioning and providing some data.

November 27, 1961. At the first meeting of the United Nations Committee on the Peaceful Uses of Outer Space, Charles W. Yost, the U.S. delegate, proposed that the WMO study the best means for worldwide dissemination of weather-satellite data through regional centers.

December 3, 1961. Tiros II was shut off.

December 4, 1961. Ambassador Adlai E. Stevenson, U.S. Representative to the United Nations, explained the U.S. program for worldwide cooperation in the peaceful uses of outer space: (1) that international law apply to outer space and celestial bodies that are free for exploration by all states and not subject to national appropriation by claim of sovereignty; (2) that the Secretary General be furnished with information on the registration of launchings, and the Secretariat perform basic service functions such as exchange of information, promotion of international cooperation, and reports on scientific and institutional developments in outer space; (3) that a worldwide effort be made under the auspices of the United Nations on programs for weather research and prediction; (4) that steps be taken to establish a global system of communication satellites; and (5) that new life and responsibilities be given the Committee on the Peaceful Uses of Outer Space.

December 11, 1961. The Political Committee of the United Nations General Assembly unanimously approved a resolution asking the Committee on the Peaceful Uses of Outer Space to meet by March 31, 1962, to begin discussions on world cooperation in space activities. The membership of the Committee on the Peaceful Uses of Outer Space was increased to 28 by adding 4 new members: Chad, Morocco, Outer Mongolia, and Sierra Leone. The Secretary General was asked to maintain records of registration of launching and to perform other functions in promoting international cooperation in space activities. Global plans for weather and communication satellites were recommended, with particular reference to the roles of the World Meteorological Organization and the International Telecommunication Union. The following principles were commended to states for their guidance:

> International law, including the United Nations Charter, applies to outer space and celestial bodies; outer space and celestial bodies are free for exploration and use by all states in conformity with international law, and are not subject to national appropriation by claim of sovereignty or otherwise.

January 1962. NASA and the Weather Bureau entered into an agreement concerning the first phase of the National Operational Meteorological Satellite System.

February 8, 1962. Tiros IV was launched by a Thor-Delta rocket from Cape Canaveral at 7:43 A.M. (e.s.t.). Good photographs and infrared data were received from the satellite, and during its first 24 hours it took high-quality pictures of ice and snow in the Great Lakes–St. Lawrence area. Tiros IV differs from Tiros III in that one of its cameras has a new lens designed to give less coverage, but with reduced distortion.

March 7, 1962. President Kennedy in a letter to Premier Khrushchev included among his suggestions for international cooperation a proposal that the United States and the Soviet Union each launch a meteorological satellite, placing them in orbits from which they could provide regular worldwide coverage. Data gathered by these satellites would be disseminated internationally.

March 12, 1962. In testimony before a subcommittee of the House Committee on Science and Astronautics, Francis W. Reichelderfer and David S. Johnson of the Weather Bureau emphasized the need for daily satellite weather observations by pointing out that if Tiros IV had been in the right location, it could have given warning of the March 7 storm that caused destruction along the eastern coast of the United States.

March 16, 1962. The Soviet Union launched a satellite, one of whose purposes, according to the *Tass* communiqué, was to investigate "the distribution and formation of cloud pattern."

March 19, 1962. The reorganized United Nations Committee on the Peaceful Uses of Outer Space held its opening meeting.

March 19, 1962. It was reported by informed sources that, effective in June, Dr. S. Fred Singer would head the meteorological-satellite activities of the Weather Bureau.

March 20, 1962. In a letter to President Kennedy, Premier Khrushchev emphasized the importance of a "world weather observation service" using meteorological satellites and urged that the United States and the Soviet Union cooperate in this field. At his news conference President Kennedy expressed gratification that Premier Khrushchev's reply pointed to "a number of areas of common interest."

March 21, 1962. Technical talks between Dr. Anatoly A. Blagonravov, a member of the Soviet Academy of Sciences, and Dr. Hugh L. Dryden, Deputy Administrator of NASA, on the subject of space cooperation between the two nations were scheduled for March 27.[*]

June 19, 1962. Tiros V was launched. By September 1962 one of its two cameras was still taking photographs of the cloud cover and transmitting them regularly to the earth. (Tiros V is still orbiting but no longer transmitting.)

September 18, 1962. Tiros VI was launched by a Thor-Delta rocket from Cape Canaveral at 4:45 A.M. It was placed into the planned orbit, traveling from 425 to 442 miles above the earth and circling the globe every 98.7 minutes. The first set of 32 pictures was taken on the second orbit as the satellite was over the eastern part of the Mediterranean Sea.

REFERENCES

1. United States Congress, the Senate (86th Congress, 1st Session), investigation of governmental organization for space activities, Hearings before the Subcommittee on Governmental Organizations for Space Activities of the Committee on Aeronautical and Space Sciences, March, April, May, 1959, p. 4.

[*] *Meteorological Satellites,* Staff Report prepared for the use of the Committee on Aeronautical and Space Sciences, United States Senate, by the Library of Congress (87th Congress, 2d Session), March, 1962, pp. 134–143.

III Chronology of Communication-
Satellite Events

October 1945. Clarke communication-satellite paper published: "Extra-Terrestrial Relays, Can Rocket Stations Give World-Wide Radio Coverage?" Arthur C. Clarke, *Wireless World,* pp. 305–308.

1946. During the year, the Signal Corps bounced radio signals against the moon, proving that relatively low power could transmit signals over great distances.

April 1955. Pierce communication-satellite paper published: "Orbital Radio Relays," John R. Pierce, *Jet Propulsion,* pp. 153–157.

July 29, 1958. National Aeronautics and Space Act adopted: Public Law 85-568, 85th Congress, H.R. [House of Representatives bill] 12575, 72 Stat. 426, 42 U.S.C. 2473.

December 18, 1958. Project Score: The first communication satellite—Project Score—was launched by the U.S. Air Force. It was equipped with radio and tape-recorder units for teletype and voice relay. On December 19, Score transmitted the voice of President Eisenhower from outer space with a Christmas message for the world. These were broadcast on 132.435 and 132.905 megacycles. Another radio on board broadcast other data on 107.970 and 107.940 megacycles. It continued to transmit for 12 days before its batteries became too weak for further use. There were 97 successful attempts to use it during its life.

April 7–10, 1959. Senate hearings: "National Aeronautics and Space Administration Authorization for Fiscal Year 1960," Part I, Scientific and Technical Presentations, S. 1582, Senate Committee on Aeronautical and Space Sciences.

April 17, 1959. House report issued: *Satellites for World Communication,* Report No. 6, House Committee on Science and Astronautics.

June 2, 1959. Senate report on authorizing appropriations to NASA: Report 332 on S. 1582 (H.R. 7007), Senate Committee on Aeronautical and Space Sciences.

June 3, 1959. President Eisenhower's voice by recording was broadcast from the Millstone Hill Radar Observatory in Westford, Massachusetts, bounced off the moon, and received at Prince Albert, Saskatchewan, where the Canadian Defense Research Board was opening a new laboratory.

March 19, 1960. Senate staff report issued: *Radio Frequency Control for Space Telecommunications.* Committee print of the Senate Committee on Aeronautical and Space Sciences.

April 29, 1960. Senate report on authorizing appropriations to NASA: Report 1300 on H.R. 10809, Senate Committee on Aeronautical and Space Sciences.

May 13, 1960. The first launching attempt at Cape Canaveral was made for the Project Echo passive communication balloon satellite, using a Thor-Delta vehicle with a take-off weight of 112,000 pounds, but it failed to orbit when the second-stage altitude controls malfunctioned. The payload was 205 pounds.

May 20 1960. FCC space-frequencies inquiry: The Federal Communications Commission established docket 13522, "In the Matter of an Inquiry Into the Allocation of Frequency Bands for Space Communications."

June 26, 1960. Pioneer V ceased transmission at a record distance of 22.5 million miles.

June 30, 1960. Senate hearings: "National Aeronautics and Space Administration Authorization for Fiscal Year 1961," Part II: Scientific and Technical Aspects of NASA Program, H.R. 10809, Senate Committee on Aeronautical and Space Sciences.

July 11, 1960. The Bell Telephone Company outlined to the Federal Communications Commission a plan for worldwide telephone and television service based upon a network of about 50 satellites in polar orbits at about 3,000 miles altitude. It was estimated that providing 600 telephone circuits plus television to 13 pairs of worldwide terminals would total $170 million. It suggested that the expense of such a system could be shared by Bell with companies abroad. These would be active repeater satellites.

August 12, 1960. Echo I launched: NASA successfully orbited passive communication satellite Echo I, a 100-foot-diameter aluminized mylar plastic balloon carrying 2 small radio beacons broadcasting on 107.94 megacycles at 10 megawatts. Echo I has been involved in more than 150 communications experiments. It demonstrated the first 2-way satellite relay telephone messages ever made across country.

August 12, 1960. President Eisenhower's voice was bounced from Goldstone, California, to Holmdel, New Jersey, by using the Echo I satellite.

August 13, 1960. The first 2-way phone conversations were held between Goldstone and Holmdel, using Echo I for reflection.

August 18, 1960. Courier I-A attempt: An attempt was made at Cape Canaveral to launch the Army's Courier I-A, an active communication satellite, using a Thor AbleStar vehicle with a take-off weight of over 105,000 pounds. The satellite weighed about 500 pounds, including about 300 pounds of electronic equipment. When the first stage developed trouble at 15 miles altitude, $2\frac{1}{2}$ minutes after launch, the vehicle was destroyed. The satellite had 19,200 solar cells, 4 transmitters, 4 receivers, and 5 tape recorders.

August 24, 1960. NASA-DOD division of responsibilities: NASA and the Department of Defense reached agreement permitting NASA to move into the active satellite field. By earlier arrangement, NASA was limited to passive satellites.

October 4, 1960. Courier I-B launched: The satellite Courier I-B, developed by the Army Signal Corps, was launched successfully by a Thor-AbleStar rocket from Cape Canaveral. A 51-inch-diameter sphere, it weighed about 500 pounds and carried 300 pounds of electronic equipment designed to operate an active repeater communication station. Courier carried 5 tape recorders for storing messages received for later delivery to points not in line of sight when the messages were received by the satellite. Its message-handling speed was 68,000 to 75,000 words per minute. One of the first messages transmitted through the satellite was sent in written form from Deal, New Jersey, and received at Ponce, Puerto Rico. Courier relayed a message from President Eisenhower to Secretary of State Herter at the United Nations. In addition to the 5 tape recorders, Courier carried 4 FM transmitters and 4 radio receivers, as well as a beacon radio transmitter at 50-megawatt power.

October 12, 1960. NASA aid to industry. NASA administrator T. Keith Glennan, in a speech in Oregon, outlined plans to accelerate American development of communication satellites, especially through provision of cost-reimbursable launching support to private industries for their experiments with communication satellites. This was one of the first NASA policy statements on government-industry cooperation in developing peaceful applications of space.

October 21, 1960. American Telephone & Telegraph Company made formal application to the Federal Communications Commission for authority to operate a communication satellite. It planned to transmit and receive at Holmdel, New Jersey, and to use the frequency band from 6,775 to 6,875 megacycles to an active repeater satellite of 175 pounds. The first version would handle simultaneously 2 2-way calls or 1 television channel. The operational version would handle 600 telephone channels or 2 television channels. The satellites would be put in a 2,200-mile-high orbit.

October 22, 1960. Courier I-B dies: Technical difficulties with Courier I-B ended its ability to retransmit signals back to earth. During the 18 days it operated, 118 million words were retransmitted. The radio beacon was still transmitting.

December 4, 1960. Senate staff report issued: *Policy Planning for Space Telecommunciations.* Committee print of the Senate Committee on Aeronautical and Space Sciences.

December 19, 1960. Westinghouse Electric Corporation announced a new ultraviolet space-communication system called "ultracom," which has the potential to a range 50 times as great as that of present radio and radar. It is expected to be less troubled with "noise" than radio, but would require relay from an orbiting satellite to another wavelength in order to penetrate to the surface of the earth.

December 31, 1960. Eisenhower communication-satellite policy: the White House released President Eisenhower's policy statement on communication satellites, urging that the government aggressively encourage private enterprise in the establishment and operation of a revenue-producing system and reporting that he had directed NASA to take the lead within the executive branch to advance research and to encourage private industry to apply its resources toward earliest possible realization of a commercial system. The President also directed NASA to cooperate closely with the FCC.

January 1961. FCC licenses I.T. & T. [International Telephone and Telegraph] for communication-satellite experiments: The FCC granted experimental licenses to the Federal Telecommunications Laboratories Division of I.T. & T. to bounce signals off the moon and orbit passive satellites for basic research, and also to the A.T. & T. to conduct an experimental program involving the transmission and reception of signals between earth terminal facilities and active communication satellites.

January 19, 1961. Lockheed seeks Justice Department concurrence in industry joint study: The Lockheed Aircraft Corporation requested approval by the Department of Justice of a proposed joint study, in conjunction with RCA Communications, Inc., General Telephone & Electronics Corporation, and perhaps other communication companies, to examine the feasibility of satellite communications and to consider the type of organization that might best develop and operate such a system.

The Justice Department on February 10 issued a "railroad release" permitting the joint study.

January 19, 1961. The Federal Communications Commission authorized A.T. & T. to establish the first space-communication link across the Atlantic on an experimental basis. Experimental satellites are expected to weigh about 175 pounds, and to orbit at 2,200 miles altitude. NASA would do the launchings, estimated to cost about $3 million each, and the company would pay about $250,000 for each of 6. The authority was for experimental work only, not a commercial system. An ultimate commercial system is estimated to require 50 satellites, 13 terminals, and an investment of $170 million.

February 10, 1961. Dr. Hugh L. Dryden talked by radiotelephone signals bounced off the moon, using the Goldstone 85-foot radio telescope at the transmitting end, and a similar new antenna at Woomers, Australia, at the receiving end.

February 28, 1961. FCC-NASA division of responsibilities: release of memorandum of understanding between FCC and NASA on respective civil space-communications activities, designed to provide a basis for coordinating the activities of the NASA and the FCC in the application of space technology to civil communications.

March 29, 1961. FCC communication-satellite-ownership inquiry: The FCC established docket 14024 in the matter of "an inquiry into the administrative and regulatory problems relating to the authorization of commercially operable space communications systems."

April 4, 1961. NASA-British-French research agreements: NASA announced that cooperative agreements had been reached with the British General Post Office and the French Center for Telecommunications Studies to provide ground stations in Europe for transmission of multichannel telephone, telegraph, and television signals using satellites to be launched by NASA during 1962 and 1963 in Projects Relay and Rebound.

April 25, 1961. NASC reactivation: Congress amended the National Aeronautics and Space Act of 1958, reactivating the National Aeronautics and Space Council in the Executive Office of the President.

May 1, 1961. GE commercial Comsat application to FCC: GE's subsidiary, Communication Satellites, Inc., filed an application with the FCC requesting authority to establish an operational communication-satellite system intended to provide worldwide interconnecting facilities for existing national telecommunications networks. [This was the first application to the FCC for an operational rather than an experimental service.]

May 5, 1961. Justice Department expresses views on

commercial joint venture: The Department of Justice replied to FCC docket 14024 setting forth certain antitrust conditions that should be considered in any plan for the development and operation of a satellite communications system:

1. All interested communication common carriers to be given an opportunity to participate in ownership of the system;

2. All interested communication common carriers be given unrestricted use on nondiscriminatory terms of the facilities of the system whether or not they elect to participate in ownership;

3. All interested parties engaged in the production and sale of communication and related equipment to be given an opportunity to participate in ownership of the system; and

4. All interested parties engaged in the production and sale of communication and related equipment be given unrestricted opportunity to furnish such equipment to the system whether or not they elect to participate in ownership.

May 8, 1961. Part I. House hearings—Science and Astronautics Committee: First 1961 group of hearings before the Committee on Science and Astronautics, U.S. House of Representatives, begun, specifically on "Communication Satellites," Representative Overton Brooks, chairman.

May 17, 1961. FCC coordination of industry frequency views: The FCC issued a draft statement and requested comments on "Preliminary Views of the United States of America—Frequency Allocations for Space Radiocommunication," prepared in cooperation with the Interdepartment Radio Advisory Committee and designed to serve as a basis for discussion with other countries preparatory to the proposed 1963 space conference of the International Telecommunications Union.

May 12, 1961. Frequency plans: IRAC-FCC Liason Representative draft "Preliminary Views of the United States of America—Frequency Allocations for Space Radio-Communication," sent to FCC in coordination.

May 18, 1961. RCA selected by NASA to build relay satellite: NASA announced the selection of RCA for contract negotiations to construct the relay experimental communication satellite to test the feasibility of transoceanic telephone, telegraph, and television communications using an active repeater satellite. The contract would amount to approximately $3,250,000. Relay is to weigh less than 100 pounds. It is to be fired into a 3,000-mile elliptical orbit by a Thor-Delta rocket system (same system used to put Tiros II [weather satellite] into orbit, November 23, 1960).

May 23, 1961. Bendix contract for tracking system: Bendix Corporation was awarded a $670,000 contract by the Navy for designing a ship-based tracking system for a communication satellite. This is a part of Project Advent. There will be 2 shore stations, 1 at Fort Dix, New Jersey, the other at Camp Roberts, California, and a mobile terminal aboard a ship. The company will combine tracking, telemetering, computer, and other equipment in a single unit.

May 24, 1961. First FCC decision favoring international carrier joint venture: FCC issued its first report based upon responses to docket 14024, stating that it favored a joint venture limited to existing common carriers engaged in international telephone and telegraph communications.

June 5, 1961. FCC-industry conference on commercial venture: FCC held a conference with representatives of international carriers, domestic carriers, and manufacturers interested in participating in a joint communication-satellite venture, and government officials, at which conference a proposal was discussed for the formation of an ad hoc committee of international carriers to develop a plan of organization for a joint venture. Justice Department urged the FCC to consider widening the base of ownership to include domestic carriers and equipment manufacturers.

June 7, 1961. Senate hearings—Aeronautical and Space Sciences Committee: Hearings began before the Committee on Aeronautical and Space Sciences, U.S. Senate, 87th Congress, 1st session, on H.R. 6874, "NASA Authorization for Fiscal Year 1962," Senator Robert S. Kerr, chairman. Communication satellites would receive $94.6 million.

June 14, 1961. House hearings—Antitrust Subcommittee No. 5 of Judiciary Committee: Hearings began before the antitrust Subcommittee No. 5, of the Judiciary Committee of the U.S. House of Representatives on "Antitrust Contempt Decrees and TV Broadcasting Industry," Representative Emanuel Celler, chairman.

June 15, 1961. Kennedy request for NASC study of commerical communication-satellite policy: President Kennedy, in a letter to Vice President Johnson, requested that the Space Council undertake to "make the necessary studies and government-wide policy recommendations for bringing into optimum use at the earliest practicable time operational communication satellites."

July 6, 1961. NASA-Douglas contract for Rebound orbit placement: NASA awarded a study contract to the Douglas

Aircraft Corporation for developing orbital-placement technicians and engineering design specifications for the Project Rebound spacecraft. Project Rebound is a passive communication-satellite program in which 3 inflated balloon-type satellites, larger and more rigid than the 100-foot Echo I, are to be placed in orbit and with 1 launch vehicle. The orbital placement technique to be developed by Douglas envisaged the injection of the satellites into 1 common circular orbit 1,500 to 2,000 miles above the earth with equal circumferential spacing between satellites during 1963.

July 13, 1961. House hearings before the Committee on Interstate and Foreign Commerce: Hearings began on "Communication Satellites" (not yet completed as of January 25, 1962), Congressman Morgan Moulder, chairman.

July 14, 1961. Part II, House hearings—Science and Astronautics Committee: Second 1961 group of hearings began before the Committee on Science and Astronautics, U.S. House of Representatives, commented specifically on "Communication Satellites," Representative Overton Brooks, chairman.

July 16, 1961. National Space Council's recommendations to the President on communication-satellite policy: The Vice President gave the President the National Space Council's recommendations on government policy on communication satellites. The Council recommended that private corporations jointly own the system, but with government regulations as to operating standards and rates to be charged. The recommendations were in response to the President's letter of June 15 to the Council.

July 21, 1961. FCC establishment of Ad Hoc Carrier Committee: FCC issued supplemental notice of inquiry (docket 14024) establishing the Ad Hoc Carrier Committee composed of international carriers, and setting forth certain public-interest objectives which the plan of organization and operation of any joint venture would be expected to satisfy and accommodate.

Membership of committee:

American Cable & Radio Corp.

American Telephone & Telegraph Co.

Hawaiian Telephone Co.

Press Wireless, Inc.

Radio Corporation of Puerto Rico.

RCA Communications, Inc.

South Puerto Rico Sugar Co.

Tropical Radio Telegraph Co.

United States-Liberia Corp. (Did not participate)

Western Union Telegraph Co.

July 24, 1961. President issued communication-satellite policy: President Kennedy issued a policy statement on communication satellites, favoring private ownership and operation of the system providing certain public-policy requirements are met.

July 27, 1961. NASA-A.T. & T. agreement on Telstar: NASA agreed to make available to A.T. & T., at cost, facilities and services for launching and tracking the low-orbit active satellites A.T. & T. is building at its own expense. A.T. & T. is prepared to spend from $15 to $25 million on this experiment prior to any final decision regarding ultimate ownership and control of the operational system.

This contract does not commit NASA with respect to any operational undertaking or any particular design of operational satellites.

August 1, 1961. Part I, Senate hearings, Communications Subcommittee: First 1961 groups of hearings before the Communications Subcommittee of the Committee on Commerce, United States Senate, began on "Space Communications and Allocation of Radio Spectrum," Senator John O. Pastore, chairman.

August 2, 1961. Part I, Senate hearings, Monopoly Subcommittee: First 1961 group of hearings before the Subcommittee on Monopoly of the Select Committee on Small Business, United States Senate, began on ownership question regarding "Space Satellite Communications," Senator Russell B. Long, chairman.

August 4, 1961. Frequency Plans: The Federal Communications Commission and the Office of Civil and Defense Mobilization (now OEP) separately recommended to the Department of State the projection internationally of Preliminary Views of the United States of America–Frequency Allocations for Space Radiocommunication in order to obtain foreign reactions.

August 11, 1961. NASA-Hughes contract for Syncom: NASA announced its selection of the Hughes Aircraft Corporation to build Syncom, an experimental active satellite to be placed in a 22,300-mile orbit synchronous with the rotation of the earth. The satellite would weigh approximately 50 pounds. It would be lifted to the 22,300-mile altitude by a 3-stage Delta vehicle and injected into the desired orbit by an additional solid-propellant rocket attached to the spacecraft. First launch target is late 1962.

The DOD, using Project Advent facilities, will participate in Project Syncom by furnishing ground stations and performing communication experiments. The contract will amount to approximately $4 million.

August 17, 1961. NASA given $94.6 million for communication-satellite development, 1962: H.R. 7445 became Public Law 87–141, under which Congress appropriated $94,600,000 to NASA for research and development on communication satellites for fiscal year 1962.

August 24, 1961. Congressional group suggested that President postpone ownership decision: Thirty-five Congressmen, including Senators Humphrey, Kefauver, and Morse, in a joint letter to President Kennedy stated that the question of ownership of the communication-satellite system required further study and should not be prematurely decided.

September 22, 1961. GE communication-satellite bid withdrawn: GE decided "not to divert its resources into the carrier-communication field but to concentrate on its traditional role as a maker of space vehicles and allied equipment."

September 25, 1961. President informed U.N. of U.S. global communication-satellite plan: President Kennedy announced in a speech before the United Nations General Assembly that the United States would propose a global system of communication satellites linking the whole world in telegraph, telephone, radio, and television He said: "The day need not be far away when such a system will televise the proceedings of this body to every corner of the world."

October 4, 1961. President's Science Advisory Committee Report on Project West Ford: A special panel of the President's Science Advisory Committee reported that it believed the West Ford experiment would not impair the study of the skies. West Ford is a communications experiment in which dipoles (hairlike filaments) are to be released from a satellite. These filaments form a belt in space that is then usable as a way of reflecting signals between large microwave transmitters and sensitive receivers. The panel concluded that the experiment should proceed as planned and that it posed no added hazard to such space activities as manned space flight.

October 12, 1961. Ad Hoc Carrier Committee report filed with FCC: The Ad Hoc Carrier Committee of International Communications Carriers appointed by the FCC on July 25 filed its report with the FCC proposing a plan of organization or joint venture to establish a commercially operable communication-satellite system.

October 16, 1961. U.S. issuance of international coordination of space frequency: The Department of State, through its Telecommunications Division, issued the U.S. coordinated version of "Preliminary Views of the United States of America—Frequency Allocations for Space Radiocommunications," setting forth certain initial conclusions with regard to frequency allocations for communication satellites and other space radiocommunication needs preparatory to the proposed 1963 space conference of the International Telecommunications Union. The Department of State sent the preliminary views, etc., to American embassies to obtain foreign reactions and offered to send teams of experts to any country requesting further information.

October 22, 1961. State Department proposal on U.N. control of space: Harlan Cleveland, Assistant Secretary of State for International Organization Affairs, outlined 7-point program in speech for Founder's Day at St. Louis University. Proposal included: U.N. Charter to govern space; space not subject to national sovereignty; registry of vehicles launched; space unit in U.N. Secretariat; world weather watch; a communication-satellite system to link world.

October 23, 1961. International Telecommunications Convention effective in United States: The International Telecommunications Convention and Radio Regulations signed at Geneva, December 21, 1959, came into effect for the United States as a result of Presidential ratification. The agreement is an extension of a previous convention setting up the International Telecommunication Union, a specialized agency of the U.N., which carries on negotiations for coordinating the use of all forms of international telecommunications.

November 8, 1961. Part II. Senate Hearings—Monopoly Subcommittee: Second group of 1961 hearings before the Subcommittee on Monopoly of the Select Committee on Small Business, U.S. Senate, on Space Communications, Senator Russell B. Long, chairman. Further inquiry into ownership question and review of Ad Hoc Carrier Committee Report to FCC.

November 27, 1961. Reactivation of U.N. Space Committee: The U.N. Committee on the Peaceful Uses of Outer Space met after 2 years of inactivity. The 24-nation committee, formed 2 years ago at the unanimous recommendation of the General Assembly, had been trying unsuccessfully to convene in the face of a Soviet boycott and Soviet attacks on its structure and purposes. At its first meeting, the U.S.S.R. sent its chief delegate, Valerian A. Zorin.

November 27, 1961. U.S. proposed communication-satellite study in U.N. Space Committee: Charles W. Yost, U.S. Representative to the U.N. Committee on the Peaceful Uses of Outer Space, recommended that a study be undertaken of ways to make a communication-satellite service available to the nations of the world as soon as practicable on a global and nondiscriminatory basis. He suggested that the International Telecommunication Union at its proposed 1963 space conference consider those aspects of space communications in which international cooperation will be required, and he urged that special attention be given to the needs of less developed states for technical assistance in the development of their domestic communications facilities in order that they might make effective use of space communications.

December 20, 1961. U.N. adopts peaceful use of space resolution: The U.N. General Assembly unanimously approved resolution 1721 (XVI) calling on the Committee on Peaceful Use of Outer Space to meet early in 1962 to discuss world cooperation in that field. The resolution included a request for world cooperation in developing a system of communication satellites and invited the U.N. to consider the communications needs of the newly developing nations under its programs of technical assistance. The Soviet Union joined the rest of the space committee's 24 members in sponsoring the resolution. The resolution, substantially in final form, had been unanimously approved by the Political Committee of the General Assembly on December 11, 1961.

January 8, 1962. Project Advent antenna installed: The world's most accurate space-communications antenna installed at Project Advent ground station at Fort Dix, New Jersey. Sylvania Electric Product, Inc., is the main contractor for the development and construction of antenna for this ground station as well as the Camp Roberts, California, station. The antenna must be accurate to within 0.024°, since an error of 1° would miss the satellite by 385 miles.

January 11, 1962. Proposed legislation—Kerr Bill: Senator Robert S. Kerr, chairman of the Senate Committee on Aeronautical and Space Sciences, introduced in the Senate his bill, S. 2650, to amend the National Aeronautics and Space Administration Act of 1958 with respect to space communications. The bill would establish a Satellite Communications Corporation made up of U.S. communications common carriers, which would own and operate a communication-satellite system. The draft, substantially in accord with the bill as introduced, had been publicized on November 28, 1961.

January 11, 1962. Presidential report to Congress on communication-satellite plans: President Kennedy, in his State of the Union message to Congress, announced his intention to send to the Congress "a measure to govern the financing and operation of an international communication-satellite system, in a manner consistent with the public interest and our foreign policy."

February 7, 1962. Presidential message to Congress: President Kennedy sent to Congress his long-awaited message and proposed bill on communication satellites. Introduced in the Senate by Senators Kerr and Magnuson, S. 2814, and in the House by Representative George P. Miller, H. R. 10138.*

July 10, 1962. Launching of Telstar, communication satellite developed by A.T.&T. and launched by NASA under contract, using a Thor-Delta rocket. Weight of satellite, 170 pounds, spherical, with a diameter of 34.5 inches. Apogee, 3502 miles, perigee, 593 miles, orbital period, 158 minutes, inclination of orbit to equator, 44.7°. Expected useful lifetime is 2 years; lifetime as a satellite is indefinite.

* *Communication Satellites: Technical, Economic, and International Developments,* Staff Report, prepared for the use of the Committee on Aeronautical and Space Sciences, United States Senate (87th Congress, 2d Session), February 25, 1962.

Glossary of Space Terms

Ablating material. A material designed to dissipate heat by vaporizing or melting. Ablating materials are used on the surfaces of some re-entry vehicles. Ablating materials absorb heat by increase in temperature and change in chemical or physical state. The heat is carried away from the surface by a loss of mass (liquid or vapor). The departing mass also blocks part of the convective heat transfer to the remaining material.

Abort. To cancel or cut short a flight.

Absolute zero. The theoretical temperature at which all molecular motion ceases. "Absolute zero" may be interpreted as the temperature at which the volume of a perfect gas vanishes. . . . The value of absolute zero is now estimated to be $-273.16°$ Celsius (Centigrade), $-459.69°$ Fahrenheit, $0°$ Kelvin, and $0°$ Rankine.

Absorption. The process in which incident electromagnetic radiation is retained by a substance. A further process always results from absorption—that is, the irreversible conversion of the absorbed radiation into some other form of energy within and according to the nature of the absorbing medium. The absorbing medium itself may emit radiation, but only after an energy conversion has occurred.

Acceleration. The rate of change of velocity. Decrease in velocity is sometimes called "negative acceleration."

Accelerometer. An instrument that measures acceleration or gravitational forces capable of imparting acceleration. An accelerometer usually uses a concentrated mass (seismic mass) that resists movement because of its inertia. The displacement of the seismic mass relative to its supporting frame or container is used as a measure of acceleration.

Acquisition. 1. The process of locating the orbit of a satellite or trajectory of a space probe so that tracking or telemetry data can be gathered. 2. The process of pointing an antenna or telescope so that it is properly oriented to allow gathering of tracking or telemetry data from a satellite or space probe.

Adsorption. The adhesion of a thin film of liquid or gas to the surface of a solid substance. The solid does not combine chemically with the adsorbed substance.

Aerodynamic heating. The heating of a body produced by passage of air or other gases over the body, significant chiefly at high speeds, caused by friction and by compression processes.

Aerodynamic vehicle. A device, such as an airplane, glider, and so forth, capable of flight only within a sensible atmosphere and relying on aerodynamic forces to maintain flight. This term is used when the context calls for discrimination from "space vehicle."

Aerospace medicine. That branch of medicine dealing with the effects of flight through the atmosphere or in space upon the human body and with the prevention or cure of physiological or psychological malfunctions arising from these effects.

Aerothermodynamic border. An altitude at about 100 miles, above which the atmosphere is so rarefied that the motion of an object through it at high speeds generates no significant surface heat.

Aerothermodynamics. The study of the aerodynamic and thermodynamic problems connected with aerodynamic heating.

Agravic. Of or pertaining to a condition of no gravitation. *See* weightlessness.

Airglow. A relatively steady visible emission from the upper atmosphere, as distinguished from the sporadic emission ot aurorae.

Air sounding. The act of measuring atmospheric phenomena or determining atmospheric conditions at altitude, especially by means of apparatus carried by balloons or rockets.

Analog computer. A computing machine that works on the principle of measuring, as distinguished from counting, in which the input data are made analogous to a measurement continuum, such as voltages, linear lengths, resistances, light intensities, and so forth, which can be manipulated by the computer.

Angstrom. A unit of length, used chiefly in expressing short wavelengths. Ten billion angstroms equal 1 meter.

Annular eclipse. An eclipse in which a thin ring of the source of light appears around the obscuring body.

Anomalistic period. The interval between 2 successive perigee passages of a satellite in orbit about a primary. Also called "perigee-to-perigee period."

Aphelion. The point at which a planet or other celestial object in orbit around the sun is farthest from the sun.

Apogee. In an orbit about the earth, the point at which the satellite is farthest from the earth; the highest altitude reached by a sounding rocket.

Apogee rocket. A rocket attached to a satellite or spacecraft designed to fire when the craft is at apogee, the point farthest from the earth in orbit. The effect of the apogee rocket is to establish a new orbit farther from the earth or to allow the craft to escape from earth orbit.

Artificial gravity. A simulated gravity established within a space vehicle, as by rotating a cabin about an axis of a spacecraft, the centrifugal force generated being similar to the force of gravity.

Asteroid. One of the many small celestial bodies revolving around the sun, most of the orbits being between those of Mars and Jupiter. Also called "planetoid," or "minor planet."

Astrobiology. The study of living organisms on celestial bodies other than the earth.

Astronaut. 1. A person who occupies a space vehicle. 2. Specifically, one of the test pilots selected to participate in Project Mercury, the first United States program for manned space flight.

Astronautics. 1. The art, skill, or activity of operating space vehicles. 2. In a broader sense, the science of space flight.

Astronomical unit. In the astronomical system of measures, a unit of length usually defined as the distance from the earth to the sun, approximately 92,900,000 statute miles or 149,600,000 kilometers.

Attitude. The position or orientation of an aircraft, spacecraft, and so forth, either in motion or at rest, as determined by the relationship between its axes and some reference line or plane such as the horizon.

Azimuth. Horizontal direction or bearing.

Backup. 1. An item kept available to replace an item that fails to perform satisfactorily. 2. An item under development intended to perform the same general function performed by another item also under development.

Baker-Nunn camera. A large camera used in tracking satellites.

Ballistic trajectory. The trajectory followed by a body being acted upon only by gravitational forces and the resistance of the medium through which it passes. A rocket without lifting surfaces is in a ballistic trajectory after its engines cease operating.

Balloon-type rocket. A rocket, such as Atlas, that requires the pressure of its propellants (or other gases) within it to give it structural integrity.

Beam-rider. A craft following a beam, particularly one that does so automatically, the beam providing the guidance.

Bionics. The study of systems which function after the manner of, or in a manner characteristic of, or resembling, living systems.

Bipropellant. A rocket propellant consisting of two unmixed or uncombined chemicals (fuel and oxidizer) fed to the combustion chamber separately.

Black box. Colloquially, any unit, usually an electronic device such as an amplifier, that can be mounted in a rocket, spacecraft, or the like as a single package.

Blockhouse. (Also written "block house.") A reinforced concrete structure, often built underground or partly underground, and sometimes dome shaped, to provide protection against blast, heat, or explosion during rocket launchings or related activities; specifically, such a structure at a launch site that houses electronic-control instruments used in launching a rocket.

Boilerplate. As in "boilerplate capsule," a metal copy of the flight model, the structure or components of which are heavier than the flight model.

Boiloff. The vaporization of a cold propellant such as liquid oxygen or liquid hydrogen, as the temperature of the propellant mass rises as in the tank of a rocket being readied for launch.

Booster. Short for "booster engine" or "booster rocket."

Booster rocket. 1. A rocket engine, either solid or liquid fuel, that assists the normal propulsive system or sustainer engine of a rocket or aeronautical vehicle in some phase of its flight. 2. A rocket used to set a missile vehicle in motion before another engine takes over. (In sense 2 the term "launch vehicle" is more commonly used.)

Braking ellipses. A series of ellipses, decreasing in size due to aerodynamic drag, followed by a spacecraft in entering a planetary atmosphere. In theory, this maneuver will allow a spacecraft to dissipate energy through aerodynamic heating without burning up.

Bremsstrahlung. Electromagnetic radiation produced by the rapid change in the velocity of an electron or another fast, charged particle as it approaches an atomic nucleus and is deflected by it.

Capsule. 1. A boxlike component or unit, often sealed. 2. A small, sealed, pressurized cabin with an internal environment that will support life in a man or animal during extremely high-altitude flight, space flight, or emergency escape.

Cascade shower. A group occurrence of cosmic rays. Also called "air shower."

Cavitation. The turbulent formation of bubbles in a fluid, occurring whenever the static pressure at any point in the fluid flow becomes less than the fluid vapor pressure.

Celestial mechanics. The study of the theory of the motions of celestial bodies under the influence of gravitational fields.

Centrifuge. Specifically, a large, motor-driven apparatus with a long arm at the end of which human and animal subjects or equipment can be revolved and rotated at various speeds to simulate very closely the prolonged accelerations encountered in high-performance aircraft, rockets, and space-craft.

Chemical rocket. A rocket using chemical fuel, fuel which requires an oxidizer for combustion, such as liquid or solid rocket fuel.

Chugging. A form of combustion instability, especially in a liquid-propellant rocket engine, characterized by a pulsing operation at a fairly low frequency, sometimes defined as occurring between particular frequency limits; the noise made in this kind of combustion. Also called "chuffing."

Cislunar. (Latin *cis,* "on this side"). Of or pertaining to phenomena, projects, or activity in the space between the earth and moon, or between the earth and the moon's orbit.

Cold-flow test. A test of a liquid rocket without firing it to check or verify the efficiency of a propulsion subsystem, providing for the conditioning and flow of propellants (including tank pressurization, propellant loading, and propellant feeding).

Companion body. A nose cone, last-stage rocket, or other body that orbits along with an earth satellite.

Complex. Entire area of launch-site facilities. This includes blockhouse, launch pad, gantry, and so forth. Also referred to as a "launch complex."

Composite materials. Structural materials of metal alloys or plastics with built-in strengthening agents that may be in the form of filaments, foils, or flakes of a strong material.

Composite propellant. A solid rocket propellant consisting of a fuel and an oxidizer.

Configuration. A particular type of a specific aircraft, rocket, and so forth, which differs from others of the same model by virtue of the arrangement of its components or by the addition or omission of auxiliary equipment as "long-range configuration," "cargo configuration."

Console. An array of controls and indicators for the monitoring and control of a particular sequence of actions, as in the checkout of a rocket, a countdown action, or a launch procedure. A console is usually designed around desklike arrays. It permits the operator to monitor and control different activating instruments, data-recording instruments, or event sequencers.

Control rocket. A vernier engine, retrorocket, or other such rocket, used to guide or make small changes in the velocity of a rocket, spacecraft, or the like.

Corona. The faintly luminous outer envelope of the sun. Also called "solar corona." The corona can be observed at the earth's surface only at solar eclipse or with the coronagraph, a photographic instrument that artifically blocks out the image of the body of the sun.

Cosmic dust. Small meteoroids of a size similar to dust.

Cosmic rays. The extremely high-energy subatomic particles that bombard the atmosphere from outer space. Cosmic-ray primaries seem to be mostly protons, hydrogen nuclei, but also comprise heavier nuclei. On colliding with atmospheric particles they produce many different kinds of lower-energy secondary cosmic radiation.

COSPAR. Abbreviation for "Committee on Space Research," International Council of Scientific Unions.

Countdown. The time period in which a sequence of events is carried out to launch a rocket; the sequence of events.

Cryogenic temperature. In general, a temperature range below about $-50°C$; more particularly, temperatures within a few degrees of absolute zero.

Data reduction. Transformation of observed values into useful, ordered, or simplified information.

Debug. 1. To isolate and remove malfunctions from a device.

or mistakes from a computer routine or program. 2. Specifically, in electronic manufacturing, to operate equipment under specified environmental and test conditions in order to eliminate early failures and to stabilize equipment prior to actual use.

Deceleration. The act or process of moving, or of causing to move, with decreasing speed; the state of so moving.

Deep space probes. Spacecraft designed for exploring space to the vicinity of the moon and beyond. Deep space probes with specific missions may be referred to as "lunar probe," "Mars probe," "solar probe," and so forth.

Destruct. The deliberate action of destroying a rocket vehicle after it has been launched, but before it has completed its course. Destructs are executed when the rocket goes off its plotted course or functions in a way so as to become a hazard.

Doppler shift. The change in frequency with which energy reaches a receiver when the source of radiation or a reflector of the radiation and the receiver are in motion relative to each other. The Doppler shift is used in many tracking and navigation systems.

Dosimeter. A device, worn by persons working around radioactive material, that indicates the amount (dose) of radiation to which they have been exposed.

Drogue parachute. A type of parachute attached to a body, used to slow it down; also called "deceleration parachute," or "drag parachute."

Ebullism. The formation of bubbles, with particular reference to water-vapor bubbles in biological fluids, caused by reduced ambient pressure.

Eccentric. Not having the same center; varying from a circle, as in "eccentric orbit."

Ecological system. A habitable environment, either created artificially, such as in a manned space vehicle, or occurring naturally, such as the environment on the surface of the earth, in which man, animals, or other organisms can live in mutual relationship with each other. Ideally, the environment furnishes the sustenance for life, and the resulting waste products revert or cycle back into the environment to be used again for the continuous support of life.

Ejection capsule. 1. In an aircraft or manned spacecraft, a detachable compartment serving as a cockpit or cabin, which may be ejected as a unit and parachuted to the ground. 2. In an artificial satellite, probe, or unmanned spacecraft, a boxlike unit usually containing recording instruments or records of observed data, which may be ejected and returned to earth by a parachute or other deceleration device.

Electric propulsion. The generation of thrust for a rocket engine involving acceleration of a propellant by some electrical device such as an arc jet, ion engine, or magnetohydrodynamic accelerator.

Electromagnetic radiation. Energy propagated through space or through material media in the form of an advancing disturbance in electrical and magnetic fields existing in space or in the media. Also called simply "radiation."

Escape velocity. The radial speed which a particle or larger body must attain in order to escape from the gravitational field of a planet or star. The escape velocity from the earth is approximately 7 miles per second; from Mars, 3.2 miles per second; and from the sun, 390 miles per second. In order for a celestial body to retain an atmosphere for astronomically long periods of time, the mean velocity of the atmospheric molecules must be considerably below the escape velocity.

Exobiology. The study of living organisms existing on celestial bodies other than the earth.

Exosphere. The outermost, or topmost portion of the atmosphere.

In the exosphere, the air density is so low that the mean free path of individual particles depends upon their direction with respect to the local vertical, being greatest for upward-moving particles. It is only from the exosphere that atmospheric gases can, to any appreciable extent, escape into outer space.

Exotic fuel. Any fuel considered to be unusual, as a boron-based fuel.

Film cooling. The cooling of a body or surface, such as the inner surface of a rocket combustion chamber, by maintaining a thin fluid layer over the affected area.

Fixed satellite. An earth satellite that orbits from west to east at such a speed as to remain constantly over a given place on the earth's equator.

Free fall. 1. The fall or drop of a body, such as a rocket, not guided, not under thrust, and not retarded by a parachute or other braking device. 2. Weightlessness.

"g" or G. An acceleration equal to the acceleration of gravity, approximately 32.2 feet per second at sea level; used as a unit of stress measurement for bodies undergoing acceleration.

Gamma ray. An electromagnetic radiation of wave form emitted by a radioactive nucleus and similar to X rays but of higher energy and shorter wavelength.

Gantry. A frame structure that spans over something, as an elevated platform that runs astride a work area, supported by wheels on each side; specifically, short for "gantry crane" or "gantry scaffold."

Gantry scaffold. A massive scaffolding structure mounted on a bridge or platform supported by a pair of towers or trestles that normally run back and forth on parallel tracks, used to assemble and service a large rocket on its launching pad. Often shortened to "gantry." Also called "service tower." This structure is a latticed arrangement of girders, tubing, platforms, cranes, elevators, instruments, wiring, floodlights, cables, and ladders—all used to attend the rocket.

Generation. In any technical or technological development, as of a missile, jet engine, or the like, a stage or period that is marked by features or performances not marked, or existent, in a previous period of development or production, as in "second generation rocket."

Gravity. The force imparted by the earth to a mass on, or close to the earth. Since the earth is rotating, the force observed as gravity is the resultant of the force of gravitation and the centrifugal force arising from this rotation.

G-tolerance. A tolerance in a person or other animal, or in a piece of equipment, to an acceleration of a particular value.

Guidance. The process of directing the movements of an aeronautical vehicle or space vehicle, with particular reference to the selection of a flight path or trajectory.

Gyro. A device that utilizes the angular momentum of a spinning rotor to sense angular motion of its base about 1 or 2 axes at right angles to the spin axis. Also called "gyroscope."

Heat sink. A material capable of absorbing heat; a device utilizing such a material and used as a thermal protection device on a spacecraft or re-entry vehicle.

Hold. During a countdown: to halt the sequence of events until an impediment has been removed so that the countdown can be resumed, as in "T minus 40 and holding."

Hot test. A propulsion system test conducted by actually firing the propellants.

Hypersonic. Pertaining to speeds of Mach 5 or greater. *See* Mach number.

Igniter. Any device used to begin combustion, such as a spark plug in the combustion chamber of a jet engine, or a squib used to ignite fuel in a rocket.

Impact area. The area in which a rocket strikes the earth's surface. Used specifically in reference to the "impact area" of a rocket range.

Inertial guidance. Guidance by means of acceleration measured and integrated within the craft.

Infrared. Infrared radiation; electromagnetic radiation in the wavelength interval from the red end of the visible spectrum on the lower limit to microwaves used in radar on the upper limit.

Injection. The process of putting an artificial satellite into orbit. Also the time of such action.

Ion. An atom or molecularly bound group of atoms having an electric charge. Sometimes also a free electron or other charged subatomic particle.

Ionosphere. The part of the earth's outer atmosphere where ions and electrons are present in quantities sufficient to affect the propagation of radio waves.

Kepler's laws. The 3 empirical laws describing the motions of planets in their orbits, discovered by Johannes Kepler. These are: (1) The orbits of the planets are ellipses, with the sun at a common focus. (2) As a planet moves in its orbit, the line joining the planet and sun sweeps over equal areas in equal intervals of time. Also called "law of equal areas." (3) The squares of the periods of revolution of any two planets are proportional to the cubes of their mean distances from the sun.

Laser. (From *l*ight *a*mplification by *s*timulated *e*mission of *r*adiation.) A device for producing light by emission of energy stored in a molecular or atomic system when stimulated by an input signal.

Launch pad. The load-bearing base or platform from which a rocket vehicle is launched. Usually called "pad."

Launch vehicle. Any device that propels and guides a spacecraft into orbit about the earth or into a trajectory to another celestial body. Often called "booster."

Liquid-propellant rocket engine. A rocket engine fueled with a propellant or propellants in liquid form. Also called "liquid-propellant rocket." Rocket engines of this kind vary somewhat in complexity, but they consist essentially of one or more combustion chambers, together with the necessary pipes, valves, pumps, injectors, and so forth.

Mach number. (After Ernst Mach [1838–1916], Austrian scientist.) A number expressing the ratio of the speed of a body or of a point on a body with respect to the surrounding air or other fluid, or the speed of a flow, to the speed of sound in the medium; the speed represented by this number. If the Mach number is less than 1, the flow is called "subsonic" and local disturbances can propagate ahead of the flow. If the Mach number is greater than 1, the flow is called "supersonic" and disturbances cannot propagate ahead of the flow, with the result that shock waves form.

Main stage. 1. In a multistage rocket, the stage that develops the greatest amount of thrust, with or without booster engines. 2. In a single-stage rocket vehicle powered by 1 or more engines, the period when full thrust (at or above 90 per cent) is attained. 3. A sustainer engine, considered as a stage after booster engines have fallen away, as in "the main stage of the Atlas."

Maser. An amplifier utilizing the principle of *m*icrowave *a*mplification by *s*timulated *e*mission of *r*adiation. Emission of energy stored in a molecular or atomic system by a microwave power supply is stimulated by the input signal.

Mass ratio. The ratio of the mass of the propellant charge of a rocket to the total mass of the rocket charged with the propellant.

Mate. To fit together 2 major components of a system.

Mean free path. Of any particle, the average distance that a particle travels between successive collisions with the other particles of an ensemble.

Meteorological rocket. A rocket designed primarily for routine upper-air observation (as opposed to research) in the lower 250,000 feet of the atmosphere, especially that portion inaccessible to balloons—that is, above 100,000 feet. Also called "rocketsonde."

Mini. A contraction of "miniature" used in combination, as in "minicomponent," "miniradio," "minitransistor."

Minitrack. A satellite-tracking system consisting of a field of separate antennas and associated receiving equipment interconnected so as to form interferometers which track a transmitting beacon in the payload itself.

Missile. Any object thrown, dropped, fired, launched, or otherwise projected with the purpose of striking a target. Short for "ballistic missile," "guided missile." Missile is loosely used as a synonym for "rocket" or "spacecraft" by some careless writers.

Mock-up. A full-sized replica or dummy of something such as a spacecraft, often made of some substitute material, such as wood, and sometimes incorporating functioning pieces of equipment, such as engines.

Module. 1. A self-contained unit of a launch vehicle or spacecraft that serves as a building block for the over-all structure. The module is usually designated by its primary function, as "command module," "lunar landing module," and so forth. 2. A 1-package assembly of functionally associated electronic parts; usually a plug-in unit.

Monopropellant. A rocket propellant consisting of a single substance, especially a liquid, capable of producing a heated jet without the addition of a second substance.

Multistage rocket. A vehicle having 2 or more rocket units, each unit firing after the one in back of it has exhausted its propellant. Normally, each unit, or stage, is jettisoned after completing its firing. Also called a "multiple-stage rocket" or, infrequently, a "step rocket."

Newton's laws of motion. A set of 3 fundamental postulates forming the basis of the mechanics of rigid bodies, formulated by Newton in 1687. The first law is concerned with the principle of inertia and states that if a body in motion is not acted upon by an external force, its momentum remains constant (law of conservation of momentum). The second law asserts that the rate of change of momentum of a body is proportional to the force acting upon the body and is in the direction of the applied force. A familiar statement of this is the equation

$$F = MA,$$

where F is vector sum of the applied forces, M the mass, and A the vector acceleration of the body. The third law is the principle of action and reaction, stating that for every force acting upon a body there exists a corresponding force of the same magnitude exerted by the body in the opposite direction.

Nuclear fuel. Fissionable material of reasonably long life, used or usable in producing energy in a nuclear reactor.

Nuclear reactor. An apparatus in which nuclear fission may be sustained in a self-supporting chain reaction. Commonly called "reactor."

Occultation. The disappearance of a body behind another body of larger apparent size. When the moon passes between the observer and a star, the star is said to be occulted.

Orbit. 1. The path of a body or particule under the influence of a gravitational or other force. For instance, the orbit of a celestial body is its path relative to another body around which it revolves. 2. To go around the earth or other body in an orbit.

Orbital elements. A set of 7 parameters defining the orbit of a satellite.

Orbital period. The interval between successive passages of a satellite.

Orbital velocity. 1. The average velocity at which an earth satellite or other orbiting body travels around its primary. 2. The velocity of such a body at any given point in its orbit, as in "its orbital velocity at the apogee is less than at the perigee."

Paraglider. A flexible-winged, kitelike vehicle designed for use in a recovery system for launch vehicles or as a re-entry vehicle.

Payload. 1. Originally, the revenue-producing portion of an aircraft's load, e.g., passengers, cargo, mail, and so forth. 2. By extension, that which an aircraft, rocket, or the like carried over and above what is necessary for the operation of the vehicle during its flight.

Peri. A prefix meaning near, as in "perigee."

Perigee. That orbital point nearest the earth when the earth is the center of attraction.

That orbital point farthest from the earth is called "apogee." Perigee and apogee are used by many writers in referring to orbits of satellites, especially artificial satellites, around any planet or satellite, thus avoiding coinage of new terms for each planet and moon.

Perturbation. Specifically, a disturbance in the regular motion of a celestial body, the result of a force additional to those which cause the regular motion.

Plasma. An electrically conductive gas comprised of neutral particles, ionized particles, and free electrons but which, taken as a whole, is electrically neutral.

Plasma engine. A reaction engine using magnetically accelerated plasma as propellant.

A plasma engine is a type of electrical engine.

Plasma sheath. An envelope of ionized gas that surrounds a body moving through an atmosphere at hypersonic velocities.

The plasma sheath affects transmission, reception, and diffraction of radio waves, thus is important in operational problems of spacecraft.

Pressure suit. A garment designed to provide the human body with an environment above ambient pressure so that respiratory and circulatory functions may continue normally, or nearly so, under low-pressure conditions, such as occur at high altitudes or in space without benefit of a pressurized cabin.

Pressurized. Containing air, or other gas, at a pressure that is higher than the pressure outside the container.

Prestage. A step in the action of igniting a large liquid rocket taken prior to the ignition of the full flow, and consisting of igniting a partial flow of propellants into the thrust chamber.

Probe. Any device inserted in an environment for the purpose of obtaining information about the environment—specifically, an instrumented vehicle moving through the upper atmosphere or space, or landing upon another celestial body in order to obtain information about the specific environment.

Purge. To rid a line or tank of residual fluid, especially of fuel or oxygen in the tanks or lines of a rocket after a test firing or simulated test firing.

Quantum theory. The theory (first stated by Max Planck before the Physical Society of Berlin on December 14, 1900) that all electromagnetic radiation is emitted and absorbed in "quanta" each of magnitude hv, h being Planck's constant and v the frequency of the radiation.

Radar astronomy. The study of celestial bodies within the solar system by means of radiation originating on earth but reflected from the body under observation. *See* radio astronomy.

Radio astronomy. The study of celestial objects through observation of radio frequency waves emitted or reflected by these objects.

Radiosonde. A balloon-borne instrument for the simultaneous measurement and transmission of meteorological data.

Reaction control system. A system of controlling the attitude of a craft when outside the atmosphere by using jets of gas in lieu of aerodynamic control surface.

Reaction engine. An engine that develops thrust by its reaction to ejection of a substance from it; specifically, such an engine that ejects a jet or stream of gases created by the burning of fuel within the engine. A reaction engine operates in accordance with Newton's third law of motion, that is, to every action (force) there is an equal and opposite reaction. Both rocket engines and jet engines are reaction engines.

Readout. The action of a radio transmitter transmitting data either instantaneously with the acquisition of the data or by play of a magnetic tape upon which the data have been recorded.

Readout station. A recording or receiving radio station at which data are received from a transmitter in a probe, satellite, or other spacecraft.

Recovery. The procedure or action that obtains when the whole of a satellite, or a section, instrumentation package, or other part of a rocket vehicle is recovered after a launch; the result of this procedure.

Recycle. In a countdown: To stop the count and to return to an earlier point in the countdown, as in "we have recycled, now at T minus 80 and counting." *Compare* hold.

Re-entry. The event occurring when a spacecraft or other object comes back into the sensible atmosphere after being rocketed to altitudes above the sensible atmosphere; the action involved in this event.

Re-entry vehicle. A space vehicle designed to return with its payload to earth through the sensible atmosphere.

Regenerative cooling. The cooling of a part of an engine by the propellant's being delivered to the combustion chamber; specifically, the cooling of a rocket-engine combustion chamber or nozzle by circulating the fuel or oxidizer, or both, around the part to be cooled.

Rendezvous. The event of 2 or more objects meeting at a preconceived time and place.

A rendezvous would be involved, for example, in servicing or resupplying a space station.

Retrorocket. (From "retroacting.") A rocket fitted on or in a spacecraft, satellite, or the like to produce thrust opposed to forward motion.

Rocket. 1. A projectile, pyrotechnic device, or flying vehicle propelled by a rocket engine. 2. A rocket engine.

Rocket engine. A reaction engine that contains within itself, or carries along with itself, all the substances necessary for its operation or for the consumption or combustion of its fuel, not requiring intake of any outside substance and hence capable of operation in outer space. Also called "rocket motor."

Rocket propellant. Any agent used for consumption or combustion in a rocket and from which the rocket derives its thrust, such as a fuel, oxidizer, additive, catalyst, or any compound or mixture of these. "Rocket propellant" is often shortened to "propellant."

Rocketstone. Meteorological rocket.

Rockoon. A high-altitude sounding system consisting of a small solid-propellant research rocket launched from a large plastic balloon.

The rocket is fired near the maximum altitude of the balloon flight. It is a relatively mobile rocket-sounding system, and has been used extensively from shipboard.

Satellite. 1. An attendant body that revolves about another body, the primary; especially in the solar system, a secondary body, or moon, that revolves about a planet. 2. A manmade object that revolves about a spatial body, such as Explorer I orbiting about the earth.

Scrub. To cancel a scheduled rocket firing, either before or during countdown.

Sensor. The component of an instrument that converts an input signal into a quantity which is measured by another part of the instrument. Also called "sensing element."

Sloshing. The back-and-forth splashing of a liquid fuel in its tank, creating problems of stability and control in the vehicle.

Solar cell. A photovoltaic device that converts sunlight directly into electrical energy.

Solar constant. The rate at which solar radiation is received on a surface perpendicular to the incident radiation and at the earth's mean distance from the sun, but outside the earth's atmosphere.

Solar radiation. The total electromagnetic radiation emitted by the sun.

Solid propellant. Specifically, a rocket propellant in solid form, usually containing both fuel and oxidizer combined or mixed and formed into a monolithic (not powdered or granulated) grain. *See* rocket propellant and grain.

Solid-propellant rocket engine. A rocket engine using a solid propellant. Such engines consist essentially of a combustion chamber containing the propellant, and a nozzle for the exhaust jet, although they often contain other components, as grids, liners, and so forth. *See* rocket engine.

Sonic. 1. Aerodynamics: Of or pertaining to the speed of sound; that moves at the speed of sound, as in "sonic flow"; designed to operate or perform at the speed of sound, as in "sonic leading edge." 2. Of or pertaining to sound, as in "sonic amplifier."

Sonic boom. A noise caused by the shock wave that emanates from an aircraft or other object traveling in the atmosphere at or above the speed of sound.

Sonic speed. The speed of sound; by extension, the speed of a body traveling at Mach 1. Sound travels at different speeds through different mediums and at different speeds through any given medium under different conditions of temperature, and so forth. In the standard atmosphere at sea level, sonic speed is approximately 760 miles per hour.

Sounding. 1. In geophysics, any penetration of the natural environment for scientific observation. 2. In meteorology, same as upper-air observation. However, a common connotation is that of a single complete radiosonde observation.

Sounding rocket. A rocket designed to explore the atmosphere within 4,000 miles of the earth's surface.

Space equivalent. A condition within the earth's atmosphere that is virtually identical, in terms of a particular function, with a condition in outer space. For example, at 50,000 feet the low air pressure and the scarcity of oxygen create a condition, so far as respiration is concerned, that is equivalent to a condition in outer space where no appreciable oxygen is present; thus, a physiological space equivalent is present in the atmosphere.

Space medicine. A branch of aerospace medicine concerned specifically with the health of persons who make, or expect to make, flights into space beyond the sensible atmosphere.

Space probe. *See* probe.

Space simulator. A device which simulates some condition or conditions existing in space and used for testing equipment, or in training programs.

Spatial. Pertaining to space.

Specific impulse. A performance parameter of a rocket propellant, expressed in seconds, and equal to thrust (in pounds) divided by weight flow rate (in pounds per second). *See* thrust.

Spectrometer. An instrument which measures some characteristics, such as intensity, of electromagnetic radiation as a function of wavelength or frequency.

Spectrum. 1. In physics, any series of energies arranged according to wavelength (or frequency); specifically, the series of images produced when a beam of radiant energy, such as sunlight, is dispersed by a prism or a reflecting grating. 2. Short for "electromagnetic spectrum" or for any part of it used for a specific purpose as the "radio spectrum" (10 kilocycles to 300,000 megacycles).

Sputtering. Dislocation of surface atoms of a material bombarded by high-energy atomic particles.

Stage. A propulsion unit of a rocket, especially 1 unit of a multistage rocket, including its own fuel and tanks.

Stationary orbit. An orbit in which an equatorial satellite revolves about the primary at the same angular rate as the primary rotates on its axis. From the primary, the satellite thus appears to be stationary over a point on the primary.

Sunspot. A relatively dark area on the surface of the sun, consisting of a dark central umbra and a surrounding penumbra that is intermediate in brightness between the umbra and the surrounding photosphere.

Sunspot cycle. A periodic variation in the number and area of sunspots with an average length of 11.1 years, but varying between about 7 and 17 years.

Supersonic. Pertaining to speeds greater than the speed of sound. *Compare* ultrasonic.

Sustainer engine. An engine that maintains the velocity of a missile or rocket vehicle, once it has achieved its programed velocity through use of a booster engine.

Sweep. The motion of the visible dot across the face of a cathode-ray bue, as a result of scanning deflection of the electron beam.

Synchronous satellite. An equatorial west-to-east satellite orbiting the earth at an altitude of 22,300 statute miles at which altitude it makes 1 revolution in 24 hours, synchronous with the earth's rotation.

Telemetry. The science of measuring a quantity or quantities, transmitting the measured value to a distant station, and there interpreting, indicating, or recording the quantities measured.

Terminator. The line separating illuminated and dark portions of a nonluminous body, as the moon.

Thermodynamics. The study of the relationships between heat and mechanical energy.

Topside sounder. A satellite designed to measure ion concentration in the ionosphere.

Tracking. The process of following the movement of a satellite or rocket by radar, radio, and photographic observations.

Trajectory. In general, the path traced by any body, as a rocket, moving as a result of externally applied forces.

Trajectory is loosely used to mean "flight path" or "orbit."

Transducer. A device capable of being actuated by energy from 1 or more transmission systems or media and of supplying related energy to 1 or more other transmission systems or media, as a microphone, a thermocouple, and so forth.

Transit. 1. The passage of a celestial body across a celestial meridian; usually called "meridian transit." 2. The apparent passage of a celestial body across the face of another celestial body or across any point, area, or line.

T-time. Any specific time, minus or plus, as referenced to "zero," or "launch" time, during a countdown sequence that is intended to result in the firing of a rocket propulsion unit that launches a rocket vehicle or missile.

Ultrasonic. Of or pertaining to frequencies above those that affect the human ear—that is, more than 20,000 vibrations per second.

The term "ultrasonic" may be used as a modifier to indicate a device or system intended to operate at an ultrasonic frequency.

Although "supersonic" was formerly used in acoustics synonymously with "ultrasonic," this usage is now rare.

Ultraviolet radiation. Electromagnetic radiation shorter in wavelength than visible radiation but longer than X rays; roughly, radiation in the wavelength interval between 10 and 4,000 angstroms. Ultraviolet radiation from the sun is responsible for many complex photochemical reactions characteristic of the upper atmosphere—for example, the formation of the ozone layer through ultraviolet dissocation of oxygen molecules followed by recombination to form ozone.

Umbilical cord. Any of the servicing electrical or fluid lines between the ground or a tower and an upright rocket missile or vehicle before the launch. Often shortened to "umbilical."

Upper-air observation. A measurement of atmospheric conditions aloft, above the effective range of a surface weather observation. Also called "sounding," "upper-air sounding."

Van Allen belt[s], Van Allen radiation belt[s]. (For James A. Van Allen, 1915– .) The zone[s] of high-intensity radiation surrounding the earth beginning at altitudes of approximately 500 miles.

Vernier engine. A rocket engine of small thrust used primarily to obtain a fine adjustment in the velocity and trajectory of a ballistic missile or space vehicle just after the thrust cutoff of the last propulsion engine, and used secondarily to add thrust to a booster or sustainer engine. Also called "vernier rocket."

Waveguide. A system of material boundaries capable of guiding electromagnetic waves.

Weightlessness. A condition in which no acceleration, whether of gravity or other force, can be detected by an observer within the system in question.

Any object falling freely in a vacuum is weightless, thus an unaccelerated satellite orbiting the earth is "weightless," although gravity affects its orbit. Weightlessness can be produced within the atmosphere in aircraft flying a parabolic flight path.

Zero g = weightlessness.

(*This glossary was compiled from* Short Glossary of Space Terms, *NASA, March 1962.*)

Suggestions for Further Reading

Bell, Joseph N. *Seven Into Space*. Chicago, Ill., Popular Mechanics Co., 1960. A survey of *Project Mercury* and the stories of the first 7 American astronauts.

Besserer, C. W. and Besserer, Hazel C. *Guide to the Space Age*. Englewood Cliffs, New Jersey, Prentice-Hall, 1959. A definition of over 5,000 words and phrases from astronautics, astronomy, and missilery.

Bizony, M. T. (ed.). *The Space Encyclopaedia*, London, The Artemis Press, 1957. Encyclopedia of astronomical and astronautical terms, carefully explained, with illustrations where required.

Bloomfield, Lincoln P. (ed.). *Outer Space, Prospects for Man and Society*. Englewood Cliffs, New Jersey, Prentice-Hall, 1962. Papers delivered at the Twentieth American Assembly at Arden House, Columbia University. Eight chapters by different authors with an introduction by Lincoln P. Bloomfield. In addition to practical uses, legal and international aspects are discussed.

Carter, L. J. (ed.). *Realities of Space Travel*. London, Putnam, 1957. A total of 24 chapters by 20 different authors. Though written before active space exploration got under way the book is valuable because of its careful (but popular) explanation of orbits, orbital injection, orbital descent, and related problems.

Chapman, John L. *ATLAS, The Story of a Missile*. New York, Harper & Row, 1960. The story of the development of the Atlas rocket.

Hartt, Julian. *The Mighty Thor*. New York, Duel, Sloan and Pearce, 1961. The story of the development of the Thor booster, which will become important during the Gemini program that is to succeed Project Mercury.

Johnson, Francis S. (ed.). *Satellite Environment Handbook*. Stanford, Calif., Stanford University Press, 1961. Eight chapters about the environment encountered by artificial satellites, partly technical.

King-Hele, Desmond. *Satellites and Scientific Research*. London, Routledge and Kegan Paul, 1960. Desmond King-Hele is the Principal Scientific Officer of the Royal Aircraft Establishment in Farnsborough, England.

Lapp, Ralph E. *Man and Space; The Next Decade*. New York, Harper & Row, 1961. A very fine comprehensive survey of what can confidently be expected during the time from 1960 to 1970.

Ley, Willy. *Rockets, Missiles, and Space Travel*. Rev. ed., New York, The Viking Press, 1960. Gives comprehensive background material of all phases of space flight and a history of missile development.

Newell, Homer E. *Sounding Rockets*. New York, McGraw-Hill, 1959. A collection of papers by various authors explaining the techniques used to acquire information about the upper atmosphere, the instrumentation and the various types of rockets employed for this purpose.

Ordway, Frederick I., 3rd. (ed.). *Advances in Space Science*. New York and London, Academic Press, vol. I, dated 1959, 4 volumes so far. Contributions by many authors, covering the whole field of astronautics, including space medicine. Technical.

Parry, Albert. *Russia's Rockets and Missiles*. New York, Doubleday & Company, 1960. Dr. Parry is Professor of Russian Literature and had based this comprehensive account almost exclusively on Russian source material.

Proceedings of the First National Conference on the Peaceful Uses of Space. (Tulsa, Oklahoma, May 26–27, 1961), U. S. Government (National Aeronautics and Space Administration) Publication, Washington, D. C., 1961. Contains a survey of NASA programs as well as discussions on educational and industrial problems.

Ramo, Simon (ed.). *Peacetime Uses of Outer Space*. New York, McGraw-Hill, 1961. Contains 12 chapters by 13 different authors on the application of space research to communication, navigation, astronomy, and so forth.

Soviet Writings on Earth Satellites and Space Travel. New York,

The Citadel Press, 1958. Translations of Russian articles, both technical and popular, about the first 3 Russian satellites (Sputniks I, II, and III).

Shternfeld, Ari. *Russian Space Science*. New York, Basic Books, 1959, with a foreword and epilogue by Willy Ley. Translated from the Russian by the Technical Documents Liaison Office, Wright Patterson Air Force Base, Ohio. This book is valuable, not only because of the amount of excellently presented material which it contains, but also because we can see the story through Russian eyes when reading it.

Stehling, Kurt R. *Project Vanguard*. New York, Doubleday & Company, 1961. The story of the first U. S. satellite project, written by its Propulsion Chief.

Zaehringer, Alfred J. *Soviet Space Technology*. New York, Harper & Row, 1961. A survey of Russian rocket work from 1900 to 1960.

Acknowledgments

The author would like to acknowledge the following sources of illustrations used in this volume: American Telephone and Telegraph Company for the illustrations on pp. 128, 129, 130, and 131; Bell Telephone Company, p. 148; Douglas Aircraft Company, p. 147; General Electric Company, pp. 50, 94, and 95; Goodyear Aircraft Corporation, p. 61; Hughes Aircraft Company, p. 135; International Telephone and Telegraph Company, p. 122; Lockheed Aircraft Corporation, p. 127; Lockheed Missile and Space Company, p. 146; National Aeronautics and Space Administration, pp. 40, 41, 98, 99, 100, 101, 102, 104, 105, 106, 107, 113, 133, 168, 178, 179, 180, 188, 189, 194, and 201; Radio Corporation of America, pp. 103, 108, and 111; Science, p. 144; Sovfoto, pp. 199 and 202; United Press International, pp. 47, 97, 112, and 113; U.S. Air Force, official U.S. Air Force photographs, pp. 42, 45, 51, and 93; U.S. Army, official U.S. Army photograph, p. 149; U.S. Department of Commerce, Weather Bureau, pp. 81, 82, 83, 84, and 85; U.S. Navy, official U.S. Navy photographs, pp. 62, 63, 66, and 67.

ABOUT THE EDITOR

WILLY LEY is today one of the leading authorities on rocket research and space travel. An expert at making scientific and technical principles comprehensible to the general public, he has lectured extensively on American work in space before "live," radio, and television audiences. An author of a number of distinguished books on space exploration and zoology—Mr. Ley took his academic training in zoology—he has also contributed to many scientific and popular publications.

Mr. Ley became interested in rocketry and space travel in the early 1920s and was one of the founders of the German Rocket Society in 1927. In the United States since 1935 and now an American citizen, he has been science editor of a New York newspaper, a research engineer for the Washington (D.C.) Institute of Technology, a consultant to the Department of Commerce's Office of Technical Services, and now holds a full professorship in the Science Department of Fairleigh Dickinson University.

Among his books are the by now classic *Rockets, Missiles, and Space Travel; The Exploration of Mars,* with Wernher von Braun; *The Conquest of Space; Engineers' Dreams; Exotic Zoology.*